STRATEGIC ASPECTS OF COMPETITIVE BIDDING FOR CORPORATE SECURITIES

STUDIES IN MANAGERIAL ECONOMICS

GRADUATE SCHOOL OF BUSINESS ADMINISTRATION
HARVARD UNIVERSITY

APPLIED STATISTICAL DECISION THEORY, by Howard Raiffa and Robert Schlaifer (1961)

TABLES FOR NORMAL SAMPLING WITH UNKNOWN VARIANCE: The Student Distribution and Economically Optimal Sampling Plans, by Jerome Bracken and Arthur Schleifer, Jr. (1964)

STRATEGIC ASPECTS OF COMPETITIVE BIDDING FOR CORPORATE SECURITIES, by Charles Christenson (1965)

STRATEGIC ASPECTS
OF COMPETITIVE
BIDDING FOR
CORPORATE SECURITIES

CHARLES J CHRISTENSON

Associate Professor of Business Administration
Harvard University

DIVISION OF RESEARCH

GRADUATE SCHOOL OF BUSINESS ADMINISTRATION

HARVARD UNIVERSITY

Boston 1965

FOREWORD

This monograph analyzes the decision problems encountered by investment bankers in bidding for corporate debt securities. The bidding parties are not typically individual investment banking firms but syndicates which form for the purpose of bidding on a particular issue. The syndicates are formed to permit the sharing of risk, to provide sufficient capital, and to provide distribution ability to resell the securities to the investing public.

After describing the institutional setting of the problem and also giving a case study which illustrates the dynamic process of how the individual firms of a syndicate exchange information and arrive at a group decision, the author creates an abstract version of this reality in terms of a mathematical model, or a series of mathematical models. This model is used to *understand* the strategic essential elements of the problem and their interactions, to *describe* past behavior, to *predict* future behavior, and to *prescribe* how syndicates should behave both internally and externally.

As far as the external behavior of a given syndicate is concerned, there are two major sources of uncertainty. First, there is the problem of what the other syndicates will do. This aspect of the problem can be viewed as a competitive sealed bidding problem in the theory of games. The author reviews the relevant literature in the theory of games and shows that as a gross predictive model it is rather good. However, game theory has very little to offer in prescribing how a given syndicate should behave in a given instance given a descriptive analysis of the competitive environment. The author, we believe, makes a methodological contribution in this phase of the problem. The second source of uncertainty deals with how quickly the investing public will buy up the bonds when these are sold at a given offering price and coupon rate. This aspect of the problem can be viewed as a statistical decision problem and we believe that the author's analysis of the data is imaginative and insightful.

One of the most fascinating aspects of the monograph concerns the internal rather than the external behavior of the syndicate. How should a group resolve their differing judgments about uncertainties and differing attitudes towards risk? This problem is discussed in depth and we believe that the author makes a methodological contribution to the normative theory of group behavior.

In several respects this book is similar to another book related to this series by C. Jackson Grayson, Jr.: *Decisions Under Uncertainty: Drilling Decisions by Oil and Gas Operators*, Division of Research, Harvard Business School, 1960. Both books describe in great detail the complexities of a coordinated class of decision problems; both

v

summarize the results of field interviews and by case analyses of actual situations report on descriptive behavior; both are interested in using the growing body of results in the theory of decisions under uncertainty to help *prescribe* rather than to *describe* choice behavior. The present monograph, however, does make more demands on the analytical sophistication of the reader. This was especially necessary in those parts of the book where the author himself contributed to the development of new methodology.

It seems to us that this book will be of interest to several audiences, among which would certainly be analytically oriented individuals in the following areas: (1) investment banking; (2) other industries which employ competitive sealed bidding; (3) managerial economics; (4) organization theory; (5) statistical decision theory; (6) operations research and/or management science.

Financial support for the post-doctoral phases of this study came in part from the income of endowment funds, which were given in general support of the School's research program, and in part from an allocation of a grant of the Ford Foundation for research in the field of business finance. The School is indebted to those donors for this support of its research program.

HOWARD RAIFFA
Professor of Business Administration

June 1965

ACKNOWLEDGMENTS

This monograph is an outgrowth of my doctoral dissertation. During the writing of that dissertation, I had the great privilege of working under the supervision of Professor Howard Raiffa. Whatever merit the following pages may have is due in large measure to what I have learned from him.

Professor John E. Bishop has also given generously of his time in helping me over several difficult points. Professors John W. Pratt and Arthur Schleifer, Jr., have made many helpful comments. Jerome Bracken and Charles Zartman assisted in computer programming and in processing of data. Mrs. Eleanor Mullen coped valiantly with the typographical idiosyncracies characteristic of decision theory in typing the final manuscript.

Several investment bankers were quite helpful in the early stages of my research in identifying problem areas and in increasing my familiarity with investment banking practice. In particular, I would like to thank Mr. Robert L. Harter of The First Boston Corporation; Messrs. A. B. Hager, Jr., and Lincoln J. Patton of Halsey, Stuart & Co., Inc.; and Mr. Albert H. Gordon of Kidder, Peabody & Co., Inc.

My original work on this subject was supported by a Ford Foundation Doctoral Dissertation Fellowship and by a grant of computer time from the Computation Center of Massachusetts Institute of Technology. Subsequent work was made possible by the Division of Research of the Harvard Business School. For the contents of this book, I am of course alone responsible.

CHARLES CHRISTENSON

Boston, Massachusetts
June 1965

CONTENTS

1. Introduction and Summary   **1**

  1. Scope of the Research

    1: Limitation to corporate bonds; 2: A brief review of the bidding situation; 3: Research methodology.

  2. Summary of Major Results

    1: In relation to the public; 2: In relation to the issuer; 3: Internal relationships in a bidding group.

  3. Implications of the Research

    1: Implications for management; 2: Implications for further research; The communication problem.

2. Investment Banking and Competitive Bidding   **7**

  1. Investment Banking

    1: Functions of the investment banker; 2: Historical development; 3: Syndicate procedures; 4: Competitive factors and profits.

  2. Competitive Bidding

    1: Methods of sale by issuer; 2: Historical development of competitive bidding; 3: Disputed status of competitive bidding; 4: Extent of competition in bidding.

  3. A Case Study of Competitive Bidding

    1: Preparation for the pricing decision; 2: Preliminary price meeting; 3: Final price meeting; 4: Results of bidding.

3. The External Decision Problem: Preliminaries   **28**

  1. Decision Variables

    1: Definitions and relations; 2: Institutional constraints on decision variables; 3: Conflicting interests in decision variables; 4: Reduced sets of variables used in subsequent analysis.

  2. Analysis in Extensive Form

    1: Representation by a game tree; 2: Backwards induction.

4. The Pricing Decision   **39**

  1. Analysis of the Static Pricing Problem

    1: Formulation of the problem; 2: Optimum price under uncertainty; 3: Optimum price under uncertainty with stationary demand; 4: Application of the model.

2. Analysis of the Dynamic Pricing Problem

1: Single-stage pricing problem with a boundary condition; 2: Multistage pricing problem with stationary demand; 3: Multistage pricing problem under uncertainty; 4: Application of the dynamic models.

5. The Bidding Decision: Game-Theoretic Analysis   **52**

1. Basic Concepts of the Theory of Games

1: Strategies, payoffs, and objectives; 2: Classification of games; 3: Equilibrium points of non-cooperative games; 4: Application to 2-person zero-sum games.

2. The Single-Play Bidding Game

1: Characterization of the game; 2: Pure strategy equilibrium points.

3. The Repeated-Play Bidding Game

1: Formal characteristics; 2: Stationary strategy equilibrium points; 3: Response strategies; 4: The credibility problem.

4. Relevance of the Game-Theoretic Analysis

1: Descriptive relevance of game analysis; 2: Normative relevance of the game analysis.

6. The Bidding Decision: Bayes Analysis   **72**

1. Determination of the Optimum Bid

1: Payoff function; 2: Optimality conditions; 3: Computational considerations; 4: Problems in assessment of multivariate distributions.

2. A Regression Model for Probability Assessment

1: Process model; 2: Distribution of process parameters and marginal distribution of the bid; 3: Prior-posterior analysis and updating of distributions.

3. Application of the Regression Model

1: Specification of the model; 2: Data employed; 3: Problems in measurement and data interpretation; 4: Sample statistics; 5: Illustrative computation of optimal bid; 6: Suggestions for further improvement of the model.

4. A Final Problem

7. The Group Decision Process   **90**

1. A Game as a Maximizer of Expected Utility

1: Basic notation; 2: Individual decision making under uncertainty; 3: Group preference—formal development; 4: Scaling the individual weights; 5: Group consensus of preferences or probabilities; 6: A bidding group as a maximizer of expected monetary value; 7: Comparison with other social welfare schemes.

2. The Group Decision Problem from the Manager's Point of View

1: Contrast with the preceding section; 2: The group decision game; 3: Graphic illustration of the manager's problem; 4: Distributing the slack left by dropouts; 5: Evaluation of the syndicate model.

3. Summary of the Group Decision Problem

Bibliography   **115**

STRATEGIC ASPECTS OF COMPETITIVE BIDDING
FOR CORPORATE SECURITIES

CHAPTER 1

Introduction and Summary

This monograph presents the results of *normative* research on public sealed bidding by investment banking firms. That is, the objective of the research was not to discover how investment bankers *do* act in competitive bidding situations but rather how they *should* act if they desire to achieve certain goals.

At the same time, we are interested in describing the actual behavior of investment bankers for at least three reasons:

1) The behavior of *other* investment bankers constitutes a part of the environment in which a given banker operates. Hence description of their behavior is relevant to his own decision problems.
2) It is of interest to compare the prescriptions for behavior we arrive at with the actual behavior of investment bankers. Implicitly, this comparison will result in an evaluation of the manner in which investment bankers are fulfilling their function and will indicate the areas in which improvements are most likely to be profitable.
3) Some knowledge of how investment bankers do in fact behave will be helpful in identifying the problem which must be resolved in arriving at decisions: what are the feasible alternatives, what are the constraints, what variables are of sufficient magnitude to be worth worrying about, and so on.

1.1. Scope of the Research

1.1.1. Limitation to Corporate Bonds

Public sealed bidding is required by law or by regulatory agencies in the sale of various classes of securities, particularly bonds of state and local governments ("municipals") and securities of regulated utilities and transportation companies. The current research was at least nominally limited to public utility debt securities, however, since each of the excluded classes of securities presents special problems which would have resulted in an undue expansion of the scope of the research. For example, municipal bonds are commonly issued on a "serial maturity" basis with a specified portion of each issue coming due each year during the life of the issue. This custom creates certain problems for the investment banker which can be handled analytically[1] but which we will not enter into in this monograph.

At the same time, public sealed bidding for public utility debt securities has a number of features in common with bidding for the excluded classes of securities or, indeed, for goods and services other than securities. Consequently some of the conclusions reached in this monograph have applicability beyond its stated scope. This is particularly true of the game-theoretic analysis in Chapter 5 and of the discussion of the group decision problem in Chapter 7.

While the major emphasis in the monograph is on the *bidding* or purchase aspect of the investment bankers' decision, in theory and in practice it is impossible to separate this decision from the *pricing* aspect, that is, the terms set by the bankers for the resale of the bonds. Consequently some attention has been given to pricing in Chapter 4, but the results in that chapter are less complete than those with respect to bidding.

1.1.2. A Brief Review of the Bidding Situation

The total bidding situation involves three main sets of participants:

1) The issuing company ("issuer"), which is attempting to raise capital through the sale of securities;
2) One or more bidders, consisting as a rule of groups of investment banking firms assembled for the specific purpose of bidding on a particular issue; and
3) The investing public. In the case of public utility bonds, the market consists substantially of institutional investors such as insurance companies and trust funds.

Bidding is generally initiated by the publication of an Invitation for Bids by the issuer. The invitation specifies the general characteristics of the issue, including the total par value and the maturity (the date at which the issuer agrees to redeem the bonds), and frequently a maximum and minimum range of prices which will be accepted. Other terms of the issue are covered in a bond indenture which is available to prospective bidders.

Upon publication of the invitation, or even earlier if its publication has been anticipated, investment banking firms begin to form into bidding groups, or syndicates, for the purpose of bidding on the bonds. The principal reasons for group bidding are to permit sharing of risk, to provide sufficient capital to carry the issue until it is sold, and to provide distribution ability to resell the securities. The bidding groups are usually headed by one or more members of a small group of firms which specialize in organizing and running syndicates.

Since bidding groups generally bid on issues with the intent of reoffering them to the public, each prospective bidder has the following three variables at his disposal (expressed as a percentage of par value):

1) The *offering price* at which the public will be invited to buy the bonds;

---

[1] See, for example, J. Percus and L. Quinto, "The Application of Linear Programming to Competitive Bond Bidding," *Econometrica 24*, pp. 413–428 (1956). Recent unpublished work by K. J. Cohen and F. S. Hammer generalizes the results of Percus and Quinto.

2) The *coupon rate* which determines the interest which the issuer will be required to pay to the holder of the bond each year during which it is outstanding; and

3) The *proceeds* to the issuer, or the amount which the bidder offers to pay to the issuer upon delivery of the bonds.

While the bidding group determines each of these three variables as part of its total decision, the issuer generally awards the bonds on the basis of the last two only, by calculating the *net interest cost*. The public, on the other hand, generally makes its decisions to buy the bonds on the basis of the first two only, by calculating the *yield*. Finally, the bidder's profit on the issue, if he is successful, depends upon the difference between the first and the last variables, called the *spread*.

Since each bidding group must make a single, joint determination of the three variables, a problem of group decision is presented. Some members of the group may want to make a strong bid, to increase the group's chance of winning the bid. Other members may resist, desiring more profit or a better public offering price. Frequently members drop out of a group at virtually the last minute because of dissatisfaction with the group's decision.

1.1.3. *Research Methodology*

The principal technique employed in this monograph is model-building. A mathematical model is an abstract representation of (a part of) the real world. That is, in building the model, we "map" the relevant features of the real world into a mathematical system with an analogous structure; or to put it another way, we identify the elements of the mathematical system with the features of the real world problem. If we have chosen a suitable model, then the elements of the mathematical system will bear the same (or analogous) relations to each other as do the features of the real world problem. Consequently, by manipulating the mathematical system we can predict what would happen if the corresponding real-world features were similarly varied.

Specifically, if we can describe the real-world bidding situation by an appropriate model, then by manipulating this model we can predict the effects that different bidding strategies will have on expected monetary profit (or some other appropriate criterion). This should assist in the determination of the strategy which is optimal in the sense of maximizing expected monetary profit.

To assist in the formulation of appropriate models, representatives of leading investment banking firms were interviewed. The purpose of these interviews was to develop an understanding of the factors considered important by men of experience in the industry so that these factors could be incorporated in the analysis. In addition, I observed the price meetings of one bidding group; its activities are described in the last part of Chapter 2.

For the statistical bidding model discussed in Chapter 6, extensive use was made of historical bidding data to estimate the parameters of the model; a Bayes regression technique was used which is described in that chapter.

1.2. Summary of Major Results

The principal conclusions of this monograph concern the bidding group's actions in relation to the public (the pricing decision), in relation to the issuer (the bidding decision), and in its own internal relationships (the group decision problem).

1.2.1.   In Relation to the Public

The principal decision made by a bidding group affecting the investing public is its determination of a public offering price. This decision is discussed in Chapter 4 from two points of view. First, optimum pricing is considered on the assumption that the group will select a price and then hold it indefinitely. Second, the possibility of periodic revision of the price is considered.

Using the first formulation, it is possible to derive some conclusions about the optimality of present pricing policies of investment bankers. There is reason to believe, the analysis suggests, that investment bankers are overly reluctant to carry inventories of unsold bonds. That is, it would probably pay to price bonds for resale somewhat higher than is the present practice, even at the expense of slowing down the rate of sale. This conclusion is advanced only tentatively, however, since it relies on several assumptions which are subject to further testing; on the other hand, sensitivity analysis of at least one major assumption tends to support the conclusion.

1.2.2.   In Relation to the Issuer

The issuer of the bonds is concerned primarily with the bid price. The determination of the bid price is the subject of Chapters 5 and 6.

In Chapter 5, bidding is approached from the point of view of the theory of games. Bidding can be characterized as a non-strictly competitive, non-cooperative game. By "non-strictly competitive" we mean that a set of opposing bidders would find collusion profitable, but by "non-cooperative" we imply that they are somehow prevented from colluding.

It is shown in Chapter 5 that the application of the equilibrium point concept of game theory results in predictions of bidding behavior which are consistent in the aggregate with the historical behavior of underwriting spreads. Equilibrium point "solutions" of games have the property that if all players but one are committed to choosing a strategy corresponding to an equilibrium point, then that player can do no better than to follow suit. Therefore, the conclusion that the equilibrium point theory is at least approximately valid descriptively lends it force as a normative theory as well. Yet in a broader sense the equilibrium concept has some perplexing weaknesses from a normative point of view. These are also discussed in Chapter 5.

An alternative formulation of the bidding situation, as a statistical decision problem, is given in Chapter 6. This approach is suggested in part by the existence of certain sources of uncertainty which cannot be handled adequately within a game-theoretic model.

In Chapter 6, we develop a model of the bidding behavior of opposing bidding groups. This model depends upon several unknown parameters. Through the use of available data on actual bids and an application of Bayes' theorem of probability theory, it is possible to arrive at a probability distribution over each opponent's bid on a particular issue. Thus we are enabled to calculate the bid which maximizes expected return.

1.2.3. Internal Relationships of a Bidding Group

The fact that the bidding decisions must be reached by a group of participants presents special problems, which are discussed in Chapter 7. Again two formulations are given.

In the first formulation, the decision-making process within the group is treated as a *bona fide* cooperative activity in which the final decision represents a sort of consensus of individual preferences. Granting certain assumptions, including that the amount of participation assigned each group member is not a subject of group decision, it is shown that expected monetary return is a reasonable criterion for group decision. Since this criterion is assumed in earlier chapters, this discussion in Chapter 7 helps to provide a foundation for the earlier work.

The alternative formulation of the group decision problem is as a non-cooperative game between the syndicate manager and the other participants. This formulation, it is contended in Chapter 7, is analogous to the decision process actually employed by bidding groups. Some conclusions are reached about the nature of optimal play by the manager. It is shown, however, that the non-cooperative model lacks certain desirable features of the cooperative model.

1.3. Implications of the Research

1.3.1. Implications for Management

Decision making is an important aspect of administration. Hence methods whereby the decision-making process can be improved are of interest to administrators. In this respect, the following conclusions are relevant.

(1) With respect to bidding behavior, the evidence indicates that investment bankers are performing nearly as well as they could expect to through the use of a more formal analysis. The implication here, then, is largely one of confirmation of existing patterns of action. At the same time, in what is essentially a low-profit activity, even marginal improvements in profits are worth seeking. The statistical bidding model discussed in Chapter 6, therefore, may be worth consideration.

(2) In the case of pricing policies, there is reason to believe, as noted earlier, that investment bankers are overly reluctant to carry inventories of unsold bonds. While this conclusion is still tentative and further research is suggested, if the conclusion is supported it will mean that bankers can improve their overall profitability by pricing somewhat higher even at the expense of carrying higher average inventories.

(3) Present procedures for group decision making have serious deficiencies. While these are to some extent an inevitable consequence of the time pressures under which a decision must be reached, there would be considerable advantage to a bidding group if more explicit information on the preferences of individual group members could be obtained.

1.3.2. *Implications for Further Research*

In a study with as broad a scope as this one, it did not prove possible to pursue every issue raised to a satisfactory conclusion. A number of points have been raised which require further research before more explicit advice to investment bankers is possible than that given in the preceding section. Some areas where further research appears to be most promising are discussed below.

(1) As noted in Sec. 1.1.1, less attention was given in this monograph to the pricing decision than to other aspects of the bidding problem. A number of interesting normative approaches to the pricing problem are formulated in Chapter 4, however, and there appears to be potential in developing some of these models further. This is particularly true of the dynamic model under uncertainty discussed in Sec. 4.2.3.

(2) The two alternative approaches to the bidding problem discussed in Chapters 5 and 6 represent two extremes of a spectrum of possible procedures. Game theory assumes perfect rationality of one's opponents and seeks to predict their behavior as maximizing decision makers, while statistical decision theory treats them as, in effect, an inert part of the environment. Attempts to combine elements of both approaches may produce results superior to either one alone. (Irving LaValle is currently working on this class of problems.)

(3) Further research is desirable at the procedural level in implementing several suggestions made in Chapter 7, in particular: (a) methods of obtaining more complete information on the preferences of individual members of a bidding group; and (b) methods of processing this information to reach a group choice.

1.3.3. *The Communication Problem*

At one time I had hoped to be able to present this research in a form which would be fully comprehensible to investment bankers and finance specialists generally. It soon developed that this restriction would be impractical if certain powerful analytical tools were to be employed. However, in an attempt to make this monograph accessible to as large an audience as possible, the more difficult material has generally been positioned so that the reader can skip it and still follow the main thread of the argument by reading the summaries and bridge paragraphs.

Since a number of the results lead to suggestions for further research rather than immediate practical implementation, there is perhaps no real need to make them available to a wide audience at this time. In the longer run, however, the significance of the results will depend upon whether or not those who have to make the decisions understand and accept them. I leave this as an unresolved problem.

CHAPTER 2

Investment Banking and Competitive Bidding

Before proceeding with the development of formal models of the decision problems encountered by investment bankers in bidding for corporate debt securities, we shall in this chapter describe the historical and institutional factors which influence these decisions. First, the characteristics of the investment banking industry in the United States will be discussed, together with a brief history of the development of the industry. Second, the same task will be undertaken for competitive bidding as a particular method of carrying out some investment banking functions. Finally, a case study will be presented as an illustration of how the decision problems arising in competitive bidding are now resolved by investment bankers.

2.1. Investment Banking

The finance function is an essential component of a modern industrial society. In more primitive economies, the same individual or economic unit will often simultaneously perform the acts of *saving*—the withholding from consumption of a portion of current product in order to meet future wants—and *final investment*—the acquisition of tools and other durable goods which make possible the satisfaction of these wants. Robinson Crusoe, in making his own tools, was saving part of his current product by a simultaneous act of final investment.

In today's more complex economy, the motives for saving are the same as in Robinson Crusoe's economy, but the means of saving are substantially different. Today, a substantial share of investment in tangible assets is made not by savers directly but by business and governmental organizations which must secure funds for these investments by tapping the savings of others. Even in the case of tangible investments made directly by households—in homes and consumer durables—the acquiring household frequently draws not only on its own savings but also on those of others, made available to it in the form of mortgage loans and instalment credit.

The decoupling of savings and investment creates a requirement for means to transfer resources from savers to final investors. A wide variety of financial instruments and institutions has evolved in response to this requirement. Investment banking is one of these institutions.

2.1.1. *Functions of the Investment Banker*

One of the means by which a business enterprise requiring funds for investment may tap the pool of savings is through the sale of its securities—stocks or bonds—to the public.[1] If the enterprise does decide to raise funds through a public sale of securities, it could decide to offer the securities directly to the public, but more commonly it will choose to employ an investment banker to handle the distribution of securities.   There are several reasons why it might so choose.

First of all, the investment banker is an experienced merchant of securities. He employs a sales force acquainted with this unique type of merchandise, possesses lists of customers, and has a "feel for the market" that will help him to price and place the securities advantageously.   These are much the same reasons that anyone with something to sell might have for going through a middleman.

A second reason is that the managers of the enterprise may wish to be certain of receiving the funds they require.   They are unwilling to be left "holding the bag" with a partially sold issue.   They are therefore willing to pay the small fee (relative to the size of the issue) that an investment banker will usually charge for a guaranteed price.   This "insurance" aspect of investment banking has led to the use of the term "underwriting" to describe the investment banker's function. In American investment banking, however, risk taking is really only incidental to the distribution function; it is qualitatively the same as the inventory risk assumed by any merchant, although the price risk is probably more substantial because of the small margins earned by investment bankers.   In England, on the other hand, it is common for companies to offer securities directly to the public, with investment bankers and others standing by to guarantee a minimum price to the company but not helping to distribute the issue.[2]

Not all offerings of securities through investment bankers involve "underwriting" in the sense discussed in the preceding paragraph.   In some cases, particularly those involving the securities of small or unseasoned companies, the bankers may undertake the offering on a "best efforts" basis.   This means that the sales facilities of the banker will be used in selling the issue but that the banker does not guarantee that the entire issue can be sold at the agreed price.

Investment bankers are also active in giving financial advice to companies which are considering raising new capital.   This activity is of course an important competitive tactic, since it may encourage these companies to bring their business to the banker when they have securities to sell.   Because financial planning necessarily overlaps other aspects of a business, investment bankers frequently acquire considerable experience and skill in areas other than finance.   As a result of this, as well as for other reasons, many bankers serve on boards of directors of companies they have helped to finance.

---

[1] The study of the major classes of securities and their characteristics constitutes an important part of the subject matter of finance. See, for example, A. S. Dewing, *The Financial Policy of Corporations*, 5th ed., Chs. 3–9, 21, 23.

[2] L. Loss, *Securities Regulation*, pp. 106–107.

2.1.2. *Historical Development*[3]

The first section of this chapter indicated that the importance of investment banking is a function of the degree of development of the economy. Consequently, it is not surprising that the American investment banking industry is largely a product of the period since the Civil War. In antebellum days business enterprises were mostly small and were financed with the savings of the entrepreneur and his friends. Most public capital-raising of those days was to meet the needs of governmental bodies, canals and turnpikes. These requirements were met largely through the efforts of institutions whose primary interest was in activities other than investment banking, such as commercial banks or the so-called "merchant bankers" who engaged in trade and foreign exchange.

The financing of the Civil War marked the first time that it proved necessary to raise money from the public at large on a truly broad scale. For this purpose, the Federal government enlisted the services of Jay Cooke, a Philadelphia banker who is usually credited with being the father of modern investment banking. Cooke put an army of four or five thousand salesmen into the field to tap the modest savings of the farmers, local merchants, and others who had previously hoarded their savings or deposited it in banks.

The success of Cooke's wartime efforts demonstrated the existence of heretofore unsuspected sources of funds, and Cooke's firm and others continued to exploit these sources in the immediate postwar period to finance the rapidly growing railroads. This period proved to be one of speculative excess, however, and retribution came in the panic of 1873. Cooke's firm was one of the first to go bankrupt, and the entire experience was enough to discredit direct selling of securities to the public for a quarter of a century. The practice was revived around the turn of the century by N. W. Harris.

The second major innovation of Jay Cooke was the syndicate method of distribution, whereby a group of bankers joined together in a temporary partnership for the purpose of distributing a particular issue of securities. Joint ventures had had a long history in other fields of endeavor, and even prior to the Civil War bankers had come together in joint ventures for the purpose of *purchasing* entire issues of securities. For example, the Philadelphia concern of E. W. Clark & Co., for which Cooke worked at the time, had participated in several joint purchases of U.S. Treasury bonds during the Mexican War. In these earlier instances, however, the cooperative action had ended with the consummation of the purchase; so far as the distribution of the bonds was concerned, it was every man for himself.

In connection with an 1870 issue of Pennsylvania Railroad bonds, on the other hand, the firm of Jay Cooke and Company organized a "syndicate" of eight firms which bought the bonds from the railroad at 90 and (jointly) reoffered them to the public at $92\frac{1}{2}$. Five of the eight firms assumed responsibility for the sale of the

---

[3] This section was compiled from several sources, principally: Dewing, *op. cit.*, Ch. 33; and M. H. Waterman, *Investment Banking Functions*, Chs. 2–5.

issue to the public, but the profits were to be divided among all eight members of the syndicate in proportion to subscription responsibility.[4]

Except for evolutionary modifications resulting from a changing economic and legal environment, the syndicate method of distribution has remained the predominant mode of operation in the investment banking industry to this day. It represents a novel form of adaptation to the growth of the American economy when contrasted with the experience of other industries. In many industries, large-scale enterprise has become the rule. The financing requirements of these large enterprises are also large, and this means that substantial accumulations of capital have to be available to carry inventories of securities in the process of distribution, and it must be possible to have many salesmen selling a given issue. In the development of investment banking to meet these requirements, several firms of substantial size might have developed, each having the capital and personnel within its organizations to handle even the largest issues without outside help. Instead, the typical investment banking organization has remained rather small, and the resources required to distribute a large issue are brought together by the syndicate method.

The syndicate method reached its most advanced stage of development, at least in terms of complexity, immediately prior to the passage of the various Federal securities acts in the early days of the New Deal. In the 1920's, it was common for security issues to pass through the hands of a number of syndicates between the issuer and the public. First, a "purchase syndicate" might negotiate the purchase of the issue from the corporation. Then this group would enlist the aid of a "banking group" to help carry the inventory until the sale of the securities could be arranged. Finally, a "selling group" would be organized to perform the retailing function of locating investors to buy the securities. The composition of these groups was determined largely by the special abilities of their members. The banking group, for example, would frequently include commercial banks and moneyed individuals who had the capital to carry the large inventories involved; while selling group members were selected for their ability to arrange effective distribution of the securities.[5]

The depression of the 1930's and the resultant changes in the economic and legal environment of the securities business have resulted in a considerable streamlining of syndicate procedures. For one thing, the Glass-Steagall Banking Act of 1933 forced deposit-accepting commercial banks to withdraw from the underwriting of securities (other than general obligations of state and municipal governments), thus removing from investment banking a substantial block of capital which had formerly been available for carrying inventories of securities. Second, the Federal transfer tax on the sale of securities, paid by the seller, made it desirable that the securities pass through as few changes of ownership as practicable between

---

[4] At the antitrust trial of 17 investment banking firms in the early 1950's Mr. Harold L. Stuart testified that the term "syndicate" was in use when he went to work in the business in 1895, referring to the municipal bond business which had been going on since the Civil War. *U.S.* v. *Morgan, et al.,* Transcript 13613 3/11/52 P.

[5] For a comprehensive discussion of syndicate procedures in the 1920's see Galston, *Security Syndicate Operations.*

the issuer and the investor. Third, the Federal securities acts passed in the early 1930's subjected investment bankers to civil liabilities for fraudulent statements in connection with the sale of securities underwritten by them. Prior to this development, it had been common for bankers to purchase securities "jointly and severally," meaning that each member of the purchase group accepted liability for the full amount of the issue should his partners default on their obligation to the issuer. Since the passage of the securities acts, most purchases have been "several," limiting the liability of each underwriter to his pro rata participation in the issue.

The final set of factors causing streamlined procedures have been competitive. The institutionalization of savings through life insurance, pension plans, and the like has reduced the costs of distributing securities, while simultaneously the rising influence of competitive bidding and of alternative means of corporate financing without underwriting have tended to put pressure on profit margins. These factors will be discussed at greater length later in this chapter.

2.1.3. Syndicate Procedures

The first requisite for a purchase syndicate is someone to organize and run it. This function, which is called *managing*, has tended to become the specialty of a relatively small number of investment banking houses; so much so that other investment banking firms which have "originated" issues, in the sense of making the original contact with the prospective issuer, frequently bring the proposal to one of the firms specializing in managing, rather than attempting to organize the syndicate themselves.

One reason for this specialization is that the task of organizing a syndicate requires a certain amount of detailed knowledge of procedure, and the personnel of firms specializing in managing acquire this knowledge through experience. Moreover, these personnel are usually on quite close terms with the partners or officers of other investment banking firms who will make the decisions as to whether their firms will participate in a given issue. Perhaps most important, some firms have acquired a reputation for good judgment in the evaluation of securities and for an excellent "feel" for the market. Their reputation augurs well for the success of any syndicates they lead and this naturally makes it easier for them to attract partners.

An indication of this specialization is given in Table 2.1, which gives the amount and percentage of all underwritten issues managed in the first half of 1960 by the ten firms with the largest dollar volume of managerships. If joint managers are each credited with the entire issue, these ten firms managed issues with over 99% of the dollar volume of all underwritten issues sold during the period. In terms of number of issues (rather than dollar value) the concentration was less extreme: only 27.4% of all issues were managed by these firms. (Both percentages, of course, tend to overstate the degree of concentration, since an issue jointly managed is credited in its entirety to each joint manager.)

Whether the issue has been originated within the managing firm or by another investment banker, the first task of the syndicate department of the managing firm

Table 2.1

Ten Leading Syndicate Managers, First Half 1960,
All Underwritten Corporate Issues
(dollar amounts in millions)

	Issues Managed			
	Dollar Volume*		Number of Issues	
	Amount	%	Number	%
First Boston Corporation	$ 738	21.6	32	5.1
Halsey, Stuart & Co. Inc.	465	13.6	22	3.5
White, Weld & Co.	338	9.9	25	4.0
Morgan Stanley & Co.	320	9.4	6	.9
Blyth & Co. Inc.	307	9.0	26	4.1
Lehman Brothers	295	8.6	11	1.7
Stone & Webster Securities Corp.	260	7.6	11	1.7
Merrill Lynch, Pierce, Fenner & Smith, Inc.	251	7.3	14	2.2
Kuhn, Loeb & Co.	216	6.3	9	1.4
Kidder, Peabody & Co., Inc.	208	6.1	17	2.7
All Underwritten Issues	$3,418		632	

* Where two or more firms were joint managers of an issue, the entire dollar value of the issue has been credited to each manager. Therefore, the percentage figures in the table overstate the degree of concentration.

Source: *Investment Dealers' Digest Corporate Financing Directory, First Half 1960,* August 1, 1960.

is to determine which of the many investment banking firms should be invited to participate in the purchase group and what proportion of the issue is to be assigned to each as its participation. If approached from scratch on each issue, these determinations could be quite difficult to make. As a practical expedient, the manager will usually consult the membership lists of his recent syndicates for issues of similar size and character and use these lists as the basis for enlisting members for the current syndicate.

Participations are not determined individually for each participant in the syndicate. Rather, several blocks of participants are established, with each participant within a given block having exactly the same participation as every other participant in that block. There is considerable professional jealousy about these participations, since a banker's relative position in an issue is supposed to reflect his prestige in the industry, at least as perceived by the manager. Some firms will refuse to participate in an issue unless they are included in the block with the largest participations. Other firms will refuse to participate in any issue unless they are the manager, or at least a co-manager if there are several managers.

While the practice of assigning participation to syndicate members at the time of formation of the syndicate has its origin in the consideration just discussed, it brings with it certain disadvantages. We shall show in Chapter 7 that it is virtually certain that decisions reached by the syndicate with participation preassigned are not as good as could be achieved if participation was determined at the same time as such other variables as public offering price and price to company.

As was noted earlier, it was once common for a selling *syndicate* to be organized to distribute the issue. This practice is now relatively uncommon, since purchase group members generally prefer to distribute the issue themselves rather than sharing the relatively small profit margin on the issue with another group. Where the services of additional dealers does appear desirable, the manager may organize a selling *group*. Contemporary selling groups are generally much less formal than the earlier selling syndicates. The selling group member is bound only to observe the terms of sale, and is not committed to take up any particular part of the issue, whereas the member of an old-style selling syndicate was generally liable for the distribution of a specified fraction of the issue.

According to Securities and Exchange Commission regulations, only members of the National Association of Securities Dealers may receive a commission on the sale of underwritten issues of securities. Hence the membership of the NASD, totaling 4,018 firms on June 30, 1959,[6] constitutes the group from which selling group members may be drawn.

Aside from statements required by the Securities and Exchange Commission and state regulatory agencies,[7] three main documents are involved in the underwriting of a security issue. These are: (1) the *agreement among underwriters;* (2) the *purchase agreement* between the underwriters and the issuer; and (when a selling group is used) (3) the *selling agreement* between the underwriters and members of the selling group. The latter two agreements are generally executed on behalf of the underwriters by the manager. The content of each of these three agreements is discussed briefly below.

The *agreement among underwriters* is the "constitution" of the purchase syndicate. It starts out with an identification of the issue to be purchased by the group, since each syndicate is organized for a specific issue. Second, the agreement will state the terms of sale of the issue, i.e., the basis on which sales will be made to the public. This includes of course the price at which the securities are to be sold to the public, called the *public offering price*, and all members of the syndicate agree to adhere to this price throughout the life of the syndicate agreement. The terms also include provision for settlement by each underwriter with the issuer. In addition, the manager may be empowered to "stabilize the market" by bidding for any part of the issue which is offered at less than the public offering price during the period of distribution. The purpose of stabilization is to protect the offering against temporary market setbacks resulting from the size of the issue and from speculators attempting a "raid" in hopes of making a quick profit. The selling terms will also include the "selling concession" which may be allowed to non-

---

[6] Securities and Exchange Commission, *Twenty-Fifth Annual Report*, p. 109.
[7] See Dewing, *op. cit.*, pp. 1062–1082, for a description of these requirements.

underwriting dealers who are members of the National Association of Securities Dealers. If, for example, the public offering price of a bond issue is 100 (per cent of par) and the selling concession is $\frac{1}{2}$, NASD members (including the selling departments of syndicate members) may purchase the bonds from underwriters at $99\frac{1}{2}$.

The agreement defines the expenses and other costs which the manager is permitted to charge against the syndicate accounts (which are kept by his accounting department). These expenses will include the fees paid to legal counsel for the drafting of syndicate agreements and meeting regulatory requirements. In addition, the agreement will specify the "management fee" to be paid to the manager by the syndicate members as compensation for his services.

Finally, the agreement will specify the date at which the syndicate is to terminate. Frequently the manager is given the authority to terminate the agreement in advance of the specified date or to extend the agreement beyond its scheduled termination. When the agreement is terminated, syndicate members are released from their obligation to maintain the public offering price, and if there are any unsold bonds "in syndicate" at this time, they will often be disposed of at a cut-rate price.

The *purchase agreement* begins with a comprehensive description of the proposed issue and also recites the steps taken by the company to satisfy legal requirements, such as obtaining stockholder approval if this is required by the company's charter and complying with SEC registration requirements. The agreement also states the price which the underwriters will pay to the company (*price to company*) on the date specified for settlement of the agreement. The difference between this price and the public offering price is called the *spread*, a term which will be quite important in our subsequent discussions.

Because of the waiting period imposed on securities offerings under the Federal Securities Act, for a time after passage of the Act it was customary for purchase agreements to include a so-called "market out" clause. This clause relieved the underwriters of their obligations under the agreement in the event market conditions, in the opinion of the underwriters, rendered the offering unpropitious on the scheduled date. This clause, which essentially took the underwriting risk out of "underwriting," has hardly ever been invoked in practice, and is now often omitted.

The *selling agreement* is of course required only when a selling group is used. This agreement usually recites the selling terms after the manner of the agreement among underwriters. In addition, the manager is often authorized to withhold the selling concession from dealers on any securities he has re-acquired as a result of stabilization operations, since it is considered that the dealer is entitled to the concession only when he has placed the security with a person contemplating holding it for investment purposes.

It should be mentioned that the foregoing agreements are usually drawn up by the manager's legal counsel in conjunction with counsel for the prospective issuer, and participants in the syndicate do not have much direct opportunity to influence their terms except those relating to price. The other provisions of these agreements have tended to become highly standardized, however, and "feedback" from participants dissatisfied with some of the provisions probably results in gradual change.

The foregoing discussion may be summarized by indicating the various ways in which securities under present-day procedures may find their way from the issuer to ultimate investors.   Figure 2.1 indicates the possible paths.

Figure 2.1

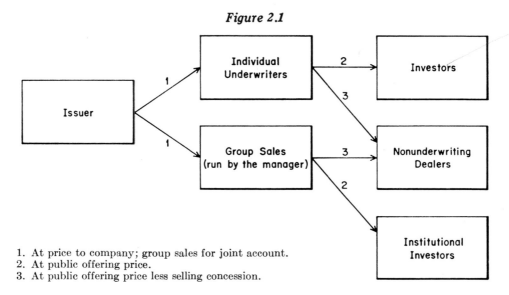

1. At price to company; group sales for joint account.
2. At public offering price.
3. At public offering price less selling concession.

There are, first of all, sales by the individual underwriters.   These may be either sales to investors at the public offering price; or sales to nonunderwriting dealers at the public offering price less the selling concession.   The dealers, in turn, will resell to investors at the public offering price.[8]

Besides the sales he makes for his own account, each underwriter will turn over a specified fraction of his participation to the manager for the purpose of "group sales."   The securities so turned over are called, in Wall Street vernacular, "the pot."   The manager sells securities from "the pot" to nonunderwriting dealers at the public offering price less the selling concession.   He also sells to large institutional investors (principally insurance companies and pension funds) at the public offering price.   Group sales are for the joint account of all the underwriters; each underwriter shares in the profits (or losses) from group sale in proportion to his participation.

The two most important decisions to be reached by a purchase syndicate are, of course, the public offering price and the price to be offered the company.   It is with these two decisions that most of the rest of this book will be concerned.   The last section of this chapter presents a case study of a syndicate arriving at a decision on a competitively bid issue.

[8] Dealers may also sell to other dealers at the public offering price less a "reallowance," which is a fraction of the selling concession.

Any member of a syndicate who is dissatisfied with the terms finally agreed upon may "drop out" before signing the agreement among underwriters. This action throws a greater burden upon the remaining members of the group, who must take up the "slack." A participant who drops out may find that this action prejudices his position in future syndicates, since some managers feel that only those participants who have shown a willingness to go along even with deals they do not quite like should be invited to participate in the next one. Other managers feel that such a policy penalizes a participant for expressing his judgment on the salability of the issue and hence hinders a free expression of opinion. They will keep drop-outs on their lists. These differences among managers will naturally affect the group decision processes, and we shall discuss them again in Chapter 7.

2.1.4.   Competitive Factors and Profits

Investment banking services are in competition with a number of other possible methods of raising long-term capital for business. The existence of these other methods tends to exert a downward pressure on investment banking costs and profits.

First of all, corporations may use funds generated by their own operations to the extent this source is adequate and thereby avoid going into the capital markets at all.

Second, corporations can sell stock or other securities on a pre-emptive basis to their own stockholders, i.e., by giving the stockholders rights entitling them to subscribe for a proportionate share of the issue. Commonly in such cases the subscription price is set substantially below the current market value of the securities. This gives the stockholders a considerable incentive either to subscribe or to sell their rights to others who will subscribe, thus eliminating much of the risk that the offering will be unsuccessful. The American Telephone and Telegraph Company in particular has used this method with considerable success.

Third, the company can sell its securities directly to institutional investors, such as insurance companies and pension funds. These institutions have grown in importance in recent years and their identity is usually well-known, so that it is not necessary to employ the sales forces of investment bankers to find them. However, companies have often found it useful to have the benefit of an investment banker's market judgment in negotiating terms for these direct placements, and it is now customary to find investment bankers acting as agents for issuers in these negotiations.

Finally, commercial banks, which once restricted their business loans largely to the financing of seasonal requirements, are now more amenable to making term loans for a period of up to ten years.

The effect of these competitive factors has been to exert a downward pressure on underwriters' spreads. This is illustrated in Table 2.2, which gives the trend of spreads over the period 1935–1958. A more complete analysis of factors affecting spreads in this period is given by Cohan.[9] In particular, it should be cautioned that the differences between negotiated and public sealed bidding transactions is in part

---

[9] A. B. Cohan, *Cost of Flotation at Long-Term Corporate Debt Since 1935*.

Table 2.2

Arithmetic Average Spread as a Per Cent of Offering Price,
by Type of Transaction, 1935–1958
(New Underwritten Corporate Debt Issues, $1 million par value and over,
rated Ba or better)

	Negotiated	Public Sealed Bidding	All Issues
1935	2.65	1.57	2.59
1936	2.45	1.01	2.37
1937	2.52	.92	2.48
1938	2.16	1.54	2.08
1939	2.23	1.23	2.15
1940	2.14	1.41	2.12
1941	1.96	1.30	1.84
1942	2.63	1.12	1.98
1943	2.37	1.15	1.84
1944	2.54	1.01	1.69
1945	1.96	.88	1.28
1946	1.36	.75	.98
1947	1.68	.69	.96
1948	1.92	.56	.70
1949	1.32	.56	.60
1950	1.50	.59	.71
1951	1.24	.74	.82
1952	1.31	.59	.81
1953	1.59	.72	.94
1954	1.06	.61	.69
1955	1.47	.63	.86
1956	1.35	.75	.97
1957	1.16	.89	.97
1958	1.18	.83	.94

SOURCE: Cohan, *Cost of Flotation of Long-Term Corporate Debt Since 1935.*

explainable on the basis of differences in the types of securities included in the two groups; public sealed bidding has been prevalent largely in the distribution of debt securities of public utilities, where spreads would be smallest in any event.

2.2. Competitive Bidding

2.2.1. *Methods of Sale by Issuer*

Assuming that an issuer has determined on an underwritten public offering of its proposed security issue, the price it is to receive for the issue may be determined in one of two ways: by *negotiation* with a single purchase syndicate it has invited to deal with it; or by the solicitation of sealed bids from any qualified syndicate which cares to submit such a bid.

In the case of negotiation, the determination of the price is largely a matter of dignified horse-trading. The representative of the prospective purchase group may propose a public offering price and a spread, which may then be met by a counterproposal from the company. This process will continue until a mutually satisfactory agreement is reached or until one party breaks off the negotiations.

If the issue is to be offered competitively, the company will publish an Invitation for Bids in the financial press. This invitation will specify the terms of the prospective issue in some detail and will also give the time and place for the submission of bids. Investment banking firms which specialize in managing issues may respond to this invitation by organizing syndicates to bid on the issue. Each syndicate will arrive at a decision on an interest rate, a public offering price, and a desired spread. A case study of the process of reaching such a decision is given in Section 2.3.

Subtracting the spread from the public offering price, the group will determine its bid. This bid will be submitted to the issuer in accordance with the terms of the invitation. If all bidders have stipulated the same interest rate, the issuer will normally award the issue to the bidder stipulating the highest price to the company. Generally, however, the company reserves the right to reject all bids or to award the issue to other than the highest bidder if it finds some flaw in the high bid.

When bonds are offered at competitive bidding, the bidding groups specify the annual interest payments to be made on the bonds as well as the price to the company. The interest is calculated at a specified *interest* or *coupon rate* which is to be applied to the par value to determine the amount of the payment. For example, 5% interest on a bond of $1,000 par value would require the corporation to pay $50 interest annually, or $25 semiannually.[10] Since it is possible that two different bidding groups will specify different coupon rates, there must be some way of standardizing bids for purposes of awarding the bonds. The method commonly followed is to award the bonds to the bidder specifying the lowest annual *cost of money* to the company, where cost of money is defined as the interest rate which equates the price to be paid to the company with the sum of (a) the present value of the principal payment to be made at maturity and (b) the present value of the semiannual coupon payments.

The practice of awarding the bonds to the bidder specifying the lowest cost of money has one disadvantage to the issuer in that it leaves uncontrolled other variables in which the issuer might be interested. Suppose, for example, that a company has received the two following bids for an issue of 35-year bonds (both bid price and coupon rate expressed as a percentage of par value). The cost of money corresponding to each bid is also given.

---

[10] On many bonds, the corporation's obligation to pay interest is evidenced by coupons attached to the bond which may be detached and presented to the corporation or its agent for payment on the specified date; hence the term "coupon rate."

	Bid Price	Coupon Rate	Cost of Money
Bid A	100.0000	4%	4.00%
Bid B	90.8004	$3\frac{1}{2}\%$	3.99%

According to the cost of money criterion, Bid B would be accepted. But Bid B brings the company over 9% less in funds than Bid A. If the company in fact needs the quantity of funds provided by Bid A, then Bid B would be quite undesirable despite its lower cost of money.

It might be possible to derive a criterion for determining the winning bid which reflected not only the cost of money but also other variables of interest to the issuer. In practice, much the same purpose is achieved by putting limits on acceptable bids. For example, the company might stipulate in the Invitation for Bids that no bid will be accepted which is for less than 99% of par value or for more than 102%. We shall examine the question of limits on bids further in Chapter 3.

Tables are published from which the cost of money for any particular combination of price to company and coupon rate can be calculated.[11] The issuer may specify the tables to be used in evaluating the bids and may also furnish copies of the tables to prospective bidders.

Negotiation is definitely the prevailing method of sale for industrial securities, there being only two cases, involving three issues, on record of industrial companies offering issues of new securities at competitive bidding.[12] On the other hand, bidding is probably the most common method of selling railroad and utility securities, since it is required by the Securities and Exchange Commission, the Interstate Commerce Commission, and many state utilities commissions for securities where these agencies have the authority to regulate the terms of sale.

2.2.2. *Historical Development of Competitive Bidding*

The exact beginnings of competitive bidding for securities are difficult to identify, but apparently the practice originated in the sale of the bonds of state and municipal governments about the time of the Civil War.[13] The rationale behind compulsory sealed bidding for municipal securities is precisely analogous to that for requiring bids on purchases by municipalities: to forestall the payment by investment bankers of gratuities to municipal officials in exchange for the financing business of the municipalities.

The Commonwealth of Massachusetts as long ago as 1870 required that the stock of electric and gas companies not taken up by stockholders under their rights to subscribe should be sold at public auction.[14] In 1919 Massachusetts

[11] For example, *Bond Bidding Tables* published by the Financial Publishing Company.

[12] These were issues of debentures and preferred stock by McKesson & Robbins, Inc., on July 2, 1941, and an issue of first mortgage bonds of Cudahy Packing Company on May 6, 1947. See *Analysis of Volume of Security Issues, 1935–49* for the period covered; this source lists five industrial issues offered at public sealed bidding, but two of these were equipment trust certificates sold by railroad car companies.

[13] F. McClintock, "Competitive Bidding," in *Fundamentals of Investment Banking*, p. 496.

[14] Mass. Gen. L. C. 164, Secs. 18, 19.

further required that electric and gas companies solicit bids on all bond issues.[15] A number of other states have since imposed similar requirements.   According to a survey taken in 1955,[16] 26 state utility commissions claimed the authority to require competitive bidding by electric and gas companies, although it is not clear from the published results of the survey whether all of these jurisdictions were actually requiring bidding.

Since 1926 the Interstate Commerce Commission has required competitive bidding for equipment trust obligations of railroads.   In 1944 this requirement was extended to virtually all railroad securities.

By far the biggest impetus to competitive bidding came with the adoption by the Securities and Exchange Commission in 1941 of Rule U-50.   Under the Public Utility Holding Company Act of 1935, the SEC had been given jurisdiction over the sale of securities of interstate utility holding companies and their subsidiary operating companies.   The Act had been passed to eliminate some of the holding company abuses of the 1920's which had culminated in widespread bankruptcies after the crash in 1929.   Among the alleged evils at which the Act was directed were: (a) excessive charges for services resulting from the absence of arm's-length bargaining; and (b) lack of economies in the raising of capital.[17]   The SEC's first attempt at attacking these problems in the distribution of securities was by the adoption of Rule U-12F2 in 1938.   This rule limited dealings between companies under the SEC's jurisdiction and investment bankers deemed to be "affiliated" with them.   The hair-splitting problem of determining what was meant by "affiliation" made the rule difficult to enforce, however, and it was replaced in 1940 by Rule U-50.   The latter rule, which is still in effect, requires companies under the SEC's jurisdiction to offer their securities at sealed bidding, unless relieved of this requirement by specific action of the SEC.

2.2.3.   *Disputed Status of Competitive Bidding*

Competitive bidding has been one of the most controversial topics in the history of investment banking.   Rule U-50 was adopted over the almost universal opposition of the investment banking industry, Halsey, Stuart & Company being the most notable exception.

Opponents of competitive bidding argue that it emphasizes the price aspect of securities distribution to the detriment of all others, in particular the advisory services an investment banker is capable of offering a company.   They agree that competitive bidding may reduce underwriting spreads, but in turn they argue that the company loses the possibility of getting expert advice on the design of its issue, proper timing to take advantage of market conditions, and so forth.

At least the more restrained proponents of competitive bidding would agree with some of these points, but would argue that public utilities securities are sufficiently standardized that the investment banker's advisory services are not

---

[15] Mass. Gen. L. C. 164, Sec. 15 (T. Ed. 1932).

[16] Halsey, Stuart & Co. Inc., *The Development of Competitive Bidding for Securities Under State and Federal Jurisdiction.*

[17] Public Utility Holding Company Act, Sec. 1 (b).

essential. Moreover, they would contend that the public interest requires that utilities obtain their funds at the lowest possible cost, and that the only way this can be assured is through the requirement of competitive bidding.

The preceding two paragraphs represent only the briefest summary of an extensive pro-and-con literature on competitive bidding. But it is not the purpose of this book to attempt to resolve this issue. Instead we shall take the requirement of competitive bidding for granted and attack the problem of what constitutes rational action by an investment banking syndicate contemplating the submission of a competitive bid.

2.2.4. *Extent of Competition in Bidding*

On any individual bond issue since the adoption of Rule U-50, anywhere from one to sixteen bids have been submitted. Table 2.3 gives the mean number

Table 2.3

Mean Number of Bids Per Issue
by Size and Industry Classification, 1941–1955
(New Corporate Debt Issues, $2 million par value and over)

Par Value of Issue, in Millions of Dollars	Industry Class			
	Public Utility	Railroad	Industrial	All Classes
$ 2.0–$ 9.9	5.8	4.2	–	5.6
10.0–24.9	5.9	3.6	2.0	5.3
25.0– 49.9	3.6	2.7	–	3.4
50.0– 99.9	2.6	2.1	–	2.5
100.0 and over	2.0	–	–	2.0
	5.1	3.2	2.0	4.8

Source: Halsey, Stuart & Co. Inc., *A Fifteen Year Record of Corporate Debt Financing in the United States.*

of bids per issue in the period 1941–1955, classified by the major factors which appear to have affected this mean.

It will be observed that, in general, the number of bids submitted on an issue varies inversely with the size of the issue. This is of course to be expected, since the larger the issue the more participants are likely to be required in a single syndicate, and thus the less opportunity there will be for other syndicates to be organized.

In view of the conclusions to be discussed in Chapter 5 regarding pressures toward collusion among competing bidding groups, it is of interest to consider the evidence on this topic. In its antitrust action against 17 leading investment banking firms a decade ago, the Federal government showed no reluctance to advance charges which it was later not able to support with evidence. One charge which it specifically disavowed, however, was that there was any collusion between competing bidding groups.[18]   On the contrary, it is the author's personal experience that bidding groups take extraordinary precautions to prevent opposing syndicates from learning of their deliberations.

On the other hand, the prevalence of the syndicate method means that a given investment banking firm will be working with one set of his colleagues today, while he may be in another group competing with some of them tomorrow.   There is thus the opportunity for a certain amount of cross-fertilization of ideas.   In particular, it is quite possible that there exists a concept of a "fair profit" for a given type of issue which is reasonably well accepted throughout the industry. We shall consider this matter again in Chapter 5.

2.3.   A Case Study of Competitive Bidding

In this section we shall present a case study of the decision-making process of one bidding group.   The procedures followed by this group are not typical in all respects.   Differences exist between groups led by different managers in such matters as the constitution of the price committee, the degree to which group members feel free to drop out, and so forth.   Nevertheless this case will suffice to illustrate the major features of the decision-making process.

The bond issue on which the bidding took place consisted of $65 million par value First and Refunding Mortgage Bonds, Series DD due June 1, 1990, of the Pacific Gas and Electric Company (PGE).   The series designation, DD, indicates that this was the thirtieth offering by PGE under the indenture covering its First and Refunding Mortgage Bonds.   PGE furnishes electric and gas service throughout most of northern and central California.

The bonds were rated Aa or the equivalent by all three of the major bond rating agencies (Moody, Fitch, and Standard and Poor).   This is the second highest quality rating.

An interesting feature of the bonds was a provision which prevented the company from calling the bonds during the first five years for the purpose of refunding them at a lower interest cost.   This provision was designed to protect the purchasers of the bonds in the event of a fall in interest rates.   Without the noncallability feature, the company could be expected to call the bonds and replace them with an issue carrying a lower interest rate if interest rates fell enough to justify the cost of refinancing.   The bonds would evidently be more valuable to investors with this noncallability provision than without it, but such features were relatively new in 1958 and so investment bankers had only limited experience to go by in evaluating them.

Sealed bids were to be submitted to the company's office in San Francisco prior to 11:30 a.m. Eastern Standard Time on Tuesday, December 2, 1958.   Bids were required to stipulate a coupon rate which was in multiples of $\frac{1}{8}$ of 1%.   The

---

[18] *U.S.* v. *Morgan, et al.*, Transcript 9836-7 10/19/51 A.

minimum acceptable bid was 99% of par value; no maximum bid was specified. The initial public offering price was required to be at least par.

In response to the Invitation to Bid, syndicates were formed by three managing firms: Blyth & Co., Inc., First Boston Corporation, and Halsey, Stuart & Co., Inc. Several days before the bidding, however, the First Boston and Halsey groups merged into a single account. This action was taken in part because of the fact that PGE had increased the size of the issue from $50 million to $65 million about one week before the bidding date. The Blyth group was aware that the First Boston and Halsey groups had merged.

In this section, we shall describe the functioning of the First Boston-Halsey, Stuart group. After the merger, this group included 194 members. Assigned participation ranged from $2,100,000 for each of the two managers down to $100,000 for many smaller firms.

2.3.1. Preparation for the Pricing Decision

Prior to the bidding date, each member firm was expected to have analyzed the market for the PGE bonds in an attempt to decide at what yield they should be offered for sale. The information that is customarily used for this purpose is of two sorts: comparative and market soundings.

Comparative analysis. New issues of securities must be sold in competition with outstanding issues traded in the secondary securities markets. One set of data which is relevant in determining the yield on a new issue, therefore, will be the yields on comparable outstanding issues.

The trick here is in determining what is "comparable." Every bond issue is unique in some respects; among the areas of difference are:

(1) Identity of issuer (i.e., PGE versus some other company);
(2) General nature of business;
(3) Maturity;
(4) Quality (not only as measured by the rating services but as subjectively perceived by potential investors);
(5) Callability (e.g., other bonds may lack the noncallability provision of the PGE bonds).

The practice in the industry is usually to select a number of bond issues available in the secondary market which are considered similar to the new issue in the aspects which influence marketability; to "spread" all the relevant information about these issues, including their yield at market price, out on a worksheet; and then to decide judgmentally how the new issues should fit into the yield structure.

It is not considered practical to price a new issue precisely "on the market" as determined by a comparative analysis. The market quotations for outstanding issues are often based on only a few thousands of dollars of transactions, in contrast with the millions of dollars worth involved in the new issue. Some price concession from the market is therefore required to move the new issue expeditiously. (In

Chapter 4 we shall take up the question of determining the optimal price concession.)

Market soundings. The success of a new offering is often determined by a relatively few large investors—principally pension funds, trust funds, and insurance companies. Hence the investment bankers are interested in determining whether or not these investors have funds to invest. Many investment banking houses try also to determine the price the customer is willing to pay. Others—for instance, The First Boston Corporation—do not solicit price views from potential customers, feeling that it is the job of the investment banker to determine the price and, moreover, that price views expressed by the customer are of little value because of an inevitable tendency to try to talk the price down.

This information is solicited by the sales force of the investment banking firms. The salesmen call on the investment officers of the buying institutions and seek to obtain "indications of interest" in the new issue. (Under SEC regulations, it is illegal to accept firm orders until the SEC has given final clearance to the issue after bids have been opened.)

The difficulty that is encountered here is that most of the large investors are not apt to tell the investment bankers the price they will pay or the exact extent of their interest in the new issue. They realize that if the bankers find a great deal of apparent interest they will be disposed to price the issue to yield less than they would if there were little interest. It is in the interest of the investors, therefore, to understate their interest.

Nevertheless, by evaluating the replies received from the large investors, the bankers may be able to improve their feel for the market for the new issue.

2.3.2. Preliminary Price Meeting

The first formal activity of the First Boston-Halsey, Stuart group was the preliminary price meeting held at 3:00 p.m. on Monday, December 1, 1958—i.e., the afternoon before the bidding. The meeting was held in the New York offices of Halsey, Stuart and was presided over by a vice president of that firm. A vice president of First Boston sat at his side.

Each member of the group was entitled to have a representative at the preliminary price meeting and about 75% of the members were represented. (A number of smaller members without offices in New York City did not find it possible to send a personal representative.)

The Halsey, Stuart representative, speaking for both co-managers, opened the meeting by describing the issue and bidding conditions, as in the introduction to this section. He then tried to give some impression of the demand for the issue, based on reports made by salesmen of the managing firms. The information given was of the following form:

> "*X* Insurance Company is interested if the price is right."
> "*Y* Bank will buy $1 million if cheap."
> "*Z* Pension fund has money to invest."

The Halsey, Stuart official also reported on the status of an $80 million Pacific Telephone issue which had been purchased by a group managed by his firm the preceding week. This issue had been reoffered to the public at a yield of 4.47%. Only about $30 million had been sold to date. The Pacific Telephone issue was not considered quite as attractive as the PGE issue, particularly in view of the noncallability feature of the latter.

Following these comments, ballots were passed out to the representatives attending the meeting. On these ballots they were to indicate:

(1) The name of their firm:
(2) The yield[19] to the public they favored; and
(3) The spread they desired.

After the ballots were collected, the results were called out individually, so that each participant had a record of the price views of the others. The exception was that the co-managers did not announce their own price views. The range of yields was approximately 4.45% to 4.60%, while the range of spreads was approximately .6% to 1.1%. If the yield range is translated into a range of public offering price, it represents a range of about 2.5%, or several times the contemplated spreads; this range can be interpreted as a measure of the uncertainty regarding the "right" price.

The meeting broke up about 4:15 p.m. Participating firms which did not wish to send a representative to the final price meeting the next morning were allowed until 5:15 p.m. to file bidding limits with the managers. These limits would stipulate what combinations of yield and spread these firms would find unacceptable. After the final decision had been made, the manager would then drop from the group any firm whose bidding limits excluded the decision reached.

2.3.3. Final Price Meeting

The final price meeting began at 10:00 a.m., Tuesday, December 2, 1958, at the Halsey, Stuart offices in New York. It is important to note that this time was only one and a half hours before bids would be opened in San Francisco. Firms having an assigned participation of $500,000 or more constituted the Price Committee and were entitled to participate in the price discussion. Other member firms, however, could have observers in attendance.

Prior to the meeting, the top officials of Halsey, Stuart and First Boston had met to plan their strategy. The purpose of this private meeting was to determine how strong they were prepared to bid and how much participation they were willing to take if other participants were unwilling to go along.

The Halsey, Stuart representative opened the meeting with the presentation of more information on demand similar to that given at the preliminary price

---

[19] *Yield* is defined as the interest rate which equates the public offering price with the sum of (a) the present value of the principal payment to be made at maturity and (b) the present value of the annual coupon payments.

meeting. He also announced that U.S. Treasury bonds had opened up $\frac{2}{32}$ to $\frac{4}{32}$ of a point that morning (equivalent to about a .01% decrease in yield).

He then suggested that, in view of the market superiority of the PGE bonds to the Pacific Telephone debentures, and since a strong demand was indicated, the bonds should be priced to yield 4.44% with a spread of .85%. He then started to call the roll of the Price Committee to determine whether this decision was acceptable. The roll call was discontinued only halfway through after the manager's proposal had met with a solid chorus of "Noes."

The chairman then proposed a 4.47% yield with the same spread. This met with a similar response, except for one firm, which indicated that it not only agreed with the proposed yield but was willing to double its participation (to $2,500,000) at that price. Several others volunteered the information that they would not agree to a yield of less than 4.50%.

The next try was for "through 4.50%," which meant any yield less than 4.50%. A number of "Yeses" were heard on this roll call, with several firms suggesting an offering price of $100\frac{1}{4}$ and a coupon of $4\frac{1}{2}$% for a yield of about 4.49%. The assigned participations of the affirmative voters totaled, however, only about $7 million out of the $25 million represented on the Price Committee.

After this roll call, the representatives of the two managers left the room, presumably to consult other officials of their firms. When they returned, the Halsey, Stuart official said that it appeared that an offering yield of less than 4.50% was "not in the cards," but in view of the fact that this was, in his opinion, a relatively favorable yield, the spread should be reduced. Consequently, he proposed a bid of 99.28 to 99.30 and a reoffering of 100 with a $4\frac{1}{2}$% coupon.

The roll call on this proposition found virtually the entire Price Committee in favor, with a number of firms requesting increased participation. Several of the firms, however, suggested that they would prefer an offering price of $100\frac{1}{4}$ to get more spread. To one such suggestion, the chairman responded that, "We'd all like more spread, but we know we can't get it," indicating a recognition of the competitive factors.

The Halsey, Stuart official then announced that the Price Committee seemed to favor a bid of 99.30 and a reoffering of 100. He next called the roll of the entire syndicate, including non-Price Committee members, to ascertain:

1) Who wanted to "drop out" of the group at this bid (in addition to those non-attendees whose bidding limits indicated they wanted to drop out).
2) Who wanted to increase his participation, and by how much.

After having elicited this information, the managers' representatives left the room to determine the final participations. The amount of increased participation desired was several times the amount of "slack" left by drop-outs.

The split decided upon by the managers gave every member who desired more bonds either an additional $100,000 or $125,000, although some requests had been for as much as $3 million. The managers split the balance among themselves, giving each of them a participation of $4,950,000 as against the $2,100,000 originally assigned.

The meeting broke up about 11:20 a.m., only ten minutes before bids were due. The bidding terms were telephoned to a Halsey, Stuart representative in San Francisco. The bid actually submitted was 99.301. The manager is customarily given the right to add additional digits, called a "tail," to the agreed bid in an effort to beat out a competing group with essentially the same price views.

2.3.4. Results of Bidding

The bids submitted by the two groups were as follows, both for $4\frac{1}{2}\%$ coupons.

| First Boston-Halsey, Stuart | 99.301 |
| Blyth & Co., Inc. | 99.2299 |

Thus the First Boston-Halsey, Stuart group was the winner. The difference of .0711 between the two bids, called the "cover," amounted to 71¢ per $1,000 bond. Alternatively, the difference amounted to approximately .005% in the cost of money to the company. In the investment banking industry, a cover of $2.50 per $1,000 or less is considered to represent close bidding.

The managers retained 20% of the issue in "the pot" for group and selected dealer sales. As noted in Sec. 2.1.3, these sales were on behalf of the entire group, and the managers did not, therefore, receive the entire spread on these bonds. All bonds retained for group sale were disposed of within 35 minutes of being placed on sale. In the investment banking business, such a speedy sellout is usually considered to be an indication that the issue was well-priced; we shall consider this opinion in greater detail in Chapter 4.

CHAPTER 3

The External Decision Problem: Preliminaries

In this and the following three chapters, we will treat each investment banking syndicate formed to bid on a corporate debt issue as a single decision-making unit. We will assume that the objective of each such group is to maximize some function (generally expected monetary profit) defined on the set of its possible decisions. Under these assumptions, we will seek to develop appropriate normative models to guide such a group in its external decision process.

Even if one accepts maximizing as appropriate in a normative theory of individual choice, the proposition that a group "should" maximize some function of its decision is by no means an empty one. We shall, therefore, find it necessary to return to this proposition in Chapter 7, where we will examine the problem of group decision more thoroughly.

3.1. Decision Variables

The external decision problem of a bidding group consists of the determination of specific numerical values for each of six interrelated variables. These variables were introduced and defined in Chapter 2, but that discussion will be recapitulated here in a more formal manner.

3.1.1. Definitions and Relations

The *offering price p* is the fraction (possibly greater than one) of the par value of the bonds at which the bidding group proposes to sell the bonds to the investing public if it wins the issue. The *coupon rate c* is the fraction of the par value of the bonds which the issuer will be committed to pay out to the bondholders each year during the life of the bonds. The *yield y* is the rate of annual interest which the bondholders will earn on the bonds if they buy them at the offering price and hold them to maturity.[1]

The *bid b* is the fraction of the par value of the bonds which the bidding group proposes to pay the issuer. The *cost of money r* to the issuing corporation is the

---

[1] Since most bond issues include provisions for sinking funds and/or optional call, even the investor who holds his bonds until they are redeemed by the company may not earn the yield implied by (3-1a) below. It is common, however, for sinking fund redemption prices to be set so as to protect the original investor's yield.

effective rate of annual interest it must pay on its proceeds from the sale of the bonds (i.e., on the amount bid by the winning bidding group).

Finally, the *spread s* is the percentage of par value which the bidding group proposes to retain from the offering price in order to cover its own expenses and profit.

We can, therefore, represent the external decision of a bidding group as an ordered 6-tuple $\mathbf{a} \equiv (p, b, s, y, r, c)$. Not all such 6-tuples represent feasible decisions, however, because the definitions of the variables imply certain relationships among them. As we shall show beginning in the next paragraph, the external decision of a bidding group will be completely determined by specifying numerical values for only three variables, provided that an appropriate set of three variables is selected for determination. Sets of three decision variables which completely determine the external decision will be called *reduced sets* and are listed in Table 3.1.

Table 3.1

Reduced Sets of Decision Variables

No.	Set	No.	Set	No.	Set
1	(p, b, y)	7	(p, y, r)	13	(b, y, c)
2	(p, b, r)	8	(p, r, c)	14	$(s, y, r)^*$
3	(p, b, c)	9	(b, s, y)	15	(s, y, c)
4	(p, s, y)	10	(b, s, r)	16	(s, r, c)
5	(p, s, r)	11	(b, s, c)	17	(y, r, c)
6	(p, s, c)	12	(b, y, r)		

* Subject to $p > b$.

In order to give a formal statement of the definitional relationships among the six decision variables, we first define:

$\phi_1(i) \equiv$ the present value at rate i per annum of \$1 received at the final maturity of a bond issue; and

$\phi_2(i) \equiv$ the present value at rate i per annum of \$1 per year received during the life of a bond issue.

Both $\phi_1(i)$ and $\phi_2(i)$ are assumed to be positive, continuously differentiable and, as present value functions, decreasing in i, so that $\phi_1'(i)$ and $\phi_2'(i)$ both exist and are negative.

The definitions of the six decision variables can then be written as the following system of equations:

$$\Phi_1(\mathbf{a}) = p - [\phi_1(y) + c\phi_2(y)] = 0 , \tag{3-1a}$$

$$\Phi_2(\mathbf{a}) = b - [\phi_1(r) + c\phi_2(r)] = 0 , \tag{3-1b}$$

$$\Phi_3(\mathbf{a}) = s - [\phi_1(y) + c\phi_2(y)] + [\phi_1(r) + c\phi_2(r)] = 0 . \tag{3-1c}$$

▶ Yield is defined implicitly by (3-1a) in terms of public offering price and coupon, while cost of money is defined implicitly by (3-1b) in terms of bid and coupon. In (3-1c), spread is defined as the difference between public offering price and bid, with the representations of these latter two quantities in terms of coupon, yield, and cost of money substituted in from (3-1a) and (3-1b). ◀

It is also reasonable in practice to require all six of the decision variables to be non-negative:

$$\mathbf{a} \geq \mathbf{0} . \tag{3-1d}$$

▶ The requirement that $s \geq 0$ implies, by virtue of (3-1c), that $\phi_1(y) \geq \phi_1(r)$, and hence, since ϕ_1 is a decreasing function, that $y \leq r$. This in turn implies, through (3-1a) and (3-1b), that $p \geq b$. ◀

The interdependence of the decision variables through the system (3-1) implies that not more than three of the variables may be fixed independently. For this reason, let us consider all possible partitions of $\mathbf{a}$ into two subsets, $\mathbf{a}_1$ and $\mathbf{a}_2$, of three variables each. There are $\binom{6}{3} = 20$ such partitions. Each such partition represents a possible parametrization of the external decision problem if, for any fixed value $\mathbf{a}_2^0$ which satisfies the system (3-1), there is a unique solution of the system which gives $\mathbf{a}_1$ in terms of $\mathbf{a}_2$. In this case, it is sufficient for the bidding group to specify $\mathbf{a}_2$; $\mathbf{a}_1$ will then be determined uniquely. We shall call such a $\mathbf{a}_2^0$ a *reduced set* of decision variables.

A sufficient condition for such a solution to exist in the neighborhood of a point $(\mathbf{a}_1^0, \mathbf{a}_2^0)$ satisfying (3-1) is that the Jacobian of (Φ_1, Φ_2, Φ_3) with respect to $\mathbf{a}_1$ does not vanish at that point.[2] In order to test which of the 20 possible partitions of $\mathbf{a}$ satisfy this condition, we give below the matrix of partial derivatives of the system (3-1), with the columns listed in the order (p, b, s, y, r, c):

$$\begin{bmatrix} 1 & 0 & 0 & -[\phi_1'(y) + c\phi_2'(y)] & 0 & -\phi_2(y) \\ 0 & 1 & 0 & 0 & -[\phi_1'(r) + c\phi_2'(r)] & -\phi_2(r) \\ 0 & 0 & 1 & -[\phi_1'(y) + c\phi_2'(y)] & [\phi_1'(r) + c\phi_2'(r)] & -[\phi_2(y) - \phi_2(r)] \end{bmatrix} . \tag{3-2}$$

It is at once apparent that the Jacobian formed from the first three columns of this matrix does not vanish anywhere, while that formed from the last three columns vanishes identically. All 20 possibilities can be readily tested by choosing successive pairs of columns and then checking whether any of the remaining columns can be expressed as a linear combination of the chosen pair. In this way we determine that:

(a) The Jacobians taken with respect to (y, r, c), (p, s, y) and (b, s, r) vanish identically;

(b) The Jacobian taken with respect to (p, b, c) vanishes along the line $p = b$ but is nonvanishing elsewhere; and

(c) The Jacobians with respect to all other triplets do not vanish anywhere.

[2] For the proof of this proposition, see Courant, *Differential and Integral Calculus*, Vol. II, p. 153.

There are therefore 16 possible reduced sets of decision variables (the complementary set to the triplets referred to in (c) above) which are valid everywhere; and one (the complementary set to (p, b, c)) which is valid everywhere if we impose the additional restriction that $p > b$. These 17 reduced sets are listed in Table 3.1.

3.1.2. *Institutional Constraints on Decision Variables*

The requirement that a solution to the bidding problem satisfy the definitional relations (3-1a)–(3-1c) is of course a constraint on the choice of the bidder. In addition to this purely technical constraint, the group's range of choice may be further restricted by terms of the Invitation to Bid or by financial custom. The most common such constraints are:

(a) The coupon rate may be constrained to be one of a discrete set of values, commonly multiples of $\frac{1}{8}$ of 1%.

(b) The bid may be constrained to lie within certain bounds.

The first constraint is often imposed by the issuer for accounting convenience, since it simplifies the calculation and payment of interest. The almost universal prevalence of this requirement in the corporate bond market must, however, also reflect a strong element of financial tradition.[3]

The second constraint gives the issuer an element of control over the amount of cash it will receive. The issuer stipulates the par value of the issue in the Invitation to Bid, but its cash proceeds will be the product of the par value and the winning bid. If the issuer merely awards the issue to the bidding group specifying the lowest cost of money, it may end up with considerably more or less cash than it requires, since the winning bid is determined not only by the cost of money but also by the coupon rate (see equation 3-1c).

If both the constraints we have just discussed are imposed on a particular issue, as is often the case, then the effect may be to remove one more variable from the set of three which can be fixed independently by the bidding group. We can illustrate the effect by an example. Suppose that a bidding group is working on a bond issue with the following specifications:

Term of issue	30 years
Minimum bid	99
Maximum bid	102
Coupon	Multiples of $\frac{1}{8}$ of 1%

Suppose also that the group has tentatively decided on an offering yield of 3.96% and a spread of 0.75%. From a table of bond values,[4] we find that the following offering prices correspond to a yield of 3.96%:

---

[3] Published bond yield tables (e.g., *Comprehensive Bond Values*) are usually tabulated for coupon rates in intervals of $\frac{1}{8}$ of 1%. Since these tables are the means of determining the prices at which bonds trade in the secondary markets, an additional argument for restricting coupon rates to a relatively few values is that it obviates the need for interpolation in the tables.

[4] *Bond Bidding Tables*, published by the Financial Publishing Company.

c	p
$3\frac{7}{8}\%$	98.5154
4%	100.6986
$4\frac{1}{8}\%$	102.8817

It can be seen that the only coupon rate consistent with the desired offering yield and spread and with the terms of the Invitation to Bid is 4%. (Recall that $b = p - s$, so that the constraints are $99 \le p - s \le 102$, or $99.75 \le p \le 102.75$). In this example, therefore, the bidding group is free to fix only the two variables yield and spread independently; all others follow from them plus the system (3-1) and the additional constraints.

The issuer's objective of controlling the amount of cash it receives could be met even more successfully by stipulating an exact bid—e.g., 100% of par value—rather than a minimum and a maximum. If such a stipulation were combined with a restriction on coupon rates, however, it could remove one more variable from the control of the bidding group and would in general make it impossible for any group to bid. In the example just given, for example, there is no set of decision variables such that (a) $y = 3.96\%$; (b) $s = 0.75\%$; (c) $b = 100\%$; and (d) c is in multiples of $\frac{1}{8}$ of 1%. If an issuer wishes to tighten its control over the amount of cash it will receive, it must give up some of its control over admissible coupon rates.

The question of how much "slack" it is necessary to leave potential bidders in setting the terms of the offering can be examined by looking at (3-1b). Holding r fixed, we see that a change of Δc in the coupon rate necessitates a change of $\Delta b = \phi_2(r)\, \Delta c$ in the bid. For a 30-year bond issue with a cost of money of about 4%, $\phi_2(r)$ will be of the order of 17.5. If $\Delta c = .00125$, then, the minimum range of bids which will be certain to include an admissible coupon rate is given by

$$\Delta b = 17.5 \times .00125 = .0219 \ .$$

In addition to cases of the sort discussed above, in which specification of a yield and a spread, when taken with the constraints, determine the coupon rate uniquely, there may be cases where several admissible coupon rates are consistent with a given yield and spread and the constraints. In the example just discussed, if the bidding group had wanted to offer the bonds at a yield of 3.97%, it would be faced with the following possibilities for coupon rate and price:

c	p
$3\frac{7}{8}\%$	98.3482
4%	100.5233
$4\frac{1}{8}\%$	102.7038

In this case, the group can get its desired spread with a coupon of either 4% or $4\frac{1}{8}\%$ and still meet the constraints. Hence there will occasionally be circumstances where it is desired to choose the best of two admissible coupon rates. This question, along with others of related interest, will be examined in the next section.

3.1.3. *Conflicting Interests in Decision Variables*

Other things being equal, the bidding group would prefer a higher spread to a lower one, investors would prefer a higher yield to a lower one, and the issuer would prefer a lower cost of money to a higher one. Thus the set (s, y, r) can be interpreted as representing the respective interests of the three major parties in a new-issue flotation.

These three variables appear together with the coupon rate c in (3-1c). Any three of the four variables in (3-1c) constitute a reduced set of decision variables. That is, three of the variables may be determined arbitrarily, whereupon (3-1c) can be solved for the fourth in terms of these three.

In the first two columns of Table 3.2, we list three reduced sets and the depend-

Table 3.2

Signs of Partial Derivatives of s, y, and r

Reduced Set	Dependent Variable	Sign of Partial Derivative with Respect to:			
		s	y	r	c^*
(y, r, c)	s		$-$	$+$	$+$
(s, r, c)	y	$-$		$+$	$+$
(s, y, c)	r	$+$	$+$		$-$

* If $y > r$; all partial derivatives vanish if $y = r$.

ent variable determined by (3-1c) in terms of these three. In the remaining columns of the table we give, for each dependent variable, the signs of the partial derivatives of that variable with respect to each variable in the reduced set. (The derivation of these results will be discussed later in this section.) For example, if (y, r, c) is the reduced set, then s is the dependent variable in (3-1c) and we observe that spread decreases as yield increases but increases as either cost of money or coupon rate increases.

The last column of Table 3.2 enables us to answer the question posed at the end of the preceding section regarding optimal choice of coupon. Other things being equal, the bidding group would prefer to make: (a) its spread s as large as possible; (b) the yield y as high as possible, to increase the attractiveness of the issue to the public; and (c) the cost of money r as low as possible, to increase its chances of winning the issue. Considering each of these variables in turn as the dependent variable and looking at its partial derivative with respect to c, we can see that each of the desired objectives stated above requires that the *highest* of the feasible coupon rates be chosen.

It should be emphasized that the conclusion just stated—that whenever a choice of coupon rates is presented, the highest should be chosen—assumes implicitly that, of all the six decision variables, only the yield influences the marketability

of the bonds.   If, for example, investors prefer discount bonds to premium bonds
having the same yield (as they might for tax reasons), then the situation becomes
more complicated; it is even possible under these circumstances that the lower
coupon will be superior on an overall basis.   We will not, however, consider this
more general case.

Once the coupon rate has been determined, either by the constraints discussed
in Section 3.1.2 or by those constraints together with some principle of choice such
as that just discussed, then the three parties concerned with the deal stand in
strict opposition to each of the other two.   For we see in Table 3.2 that, if c is
fixed, then, if r is also fixed, y and s must move inversely.   That is, for a fixed
cost of money r, the bidding group can improve the yield only at the expense of
its own spread, and vice versa.   On the other hand, r and s move together for
fixed y, and y and r move together for fixed s.   For example, for fixed yield, an
increase in the bidding group's spread necessitates an increase in the cost of money,
and vice versa.   For a fixed spread, an increase in the yield requires an increase
in cost of money, and vice versa.

The results in Table 3.2 are obtained by looking at the total differential of
(3-1c), which is

$$d\Phi_3 = ds - [\phi_1'(y) + c\phi_2'(y)]\, dy + [\phi_1'(r) + c\phi_2'(r)]\, dr$$
$$- [\phi_2(y) - \phi_2(r)]\, dc = 0 \ . \quad (3\text{-}3)$$

▶   For example, considering dy as the dependent variable in (3-3), and hence (s, r, c) as
the reduced set of decision variables, dy will depend on ds, dr, and dc in the following way:

$$dy = \frac{\partial y}{\partial s}\, ds + \frac{\partial y}{\partial r}\, dr + \frac{\partial y}{\partial c}\, dc \ .$$

Substituting this expression into (3-3) and setting the resulting coefficients of the independent
variables equal to 0, we obtain as the partial derivatives of y:

$$\frac{\partial y}{\partial s} = \frac{1}{\phi_1'(y) + c\phi_2'(y)} \ ,$$

$$\frac{\partial y}{\partial r} = \frac{\phi_1'(r) + c\phi_2'(r)}{\phi_1'(y) + c\phi_2'(y)} \ , \quad \text{and}$$

$$\frac{\partial y}{\partial c} = -\frac{\phi_2(y) - \phi_2(r)}{\phi_1'(y) + c\phi_2'(y)} \ .$$

The signs given in the second line of Table 3.2 follow from the stipulations that $\phi_1'(i)$ and
$\phi_2'(i)$ are negative; $c > 0$; and $\phi_2(y) \geq \phi_2(r)$.
   The other partial derivatives and their signs are obtained in similar fashion.   ◀

3.1.4.   Reduced Sets of Variables Used in Subsequent Analysis

Perhaps the most natural way for a bidding group to approach its external
bidding problem (as we saw in Sec. 2.3) is in terms of the reduced set of variables
(s, y, c).   First of all, it would decide on an offering yield on the basis of an analysis
of the market for the bonds.   Second, it would decide on its desired spread, con-

sidering prospective costs, desired profit, and the extent of competition expected from other groups. Third, it would determine the coupon rate dictated by the constraints, perhaps invoking some additional principle of choice such as that given in the last section. Finally, it would determine the three remaining variables in terms of these three.

For purposes of this study, however, it will generally be more convenient to use (p, b, c) as the reduced set of variables, with one of these determined by the other two in conjunction with constraints. Because there is a one-to-one correspondence between solutions expressed in terms of one reduced set of variables and those expressed in terms of any other set, this selection entails no loss of generality.

3.2. Analysis in Extensive Form

As a model of the external decision problem, we can construct a game involving a number of players and Nature (or chance). The rules of the game are as follows:

1. Each of the players (bidders) chooses a number, his *bid*. These choices are made without knowledge of the choices made by the other players.
2. A comparison is made of the bids and the player who submitted the highest bid is designated the winner.[5] The winner then makes a second choice, his offering price.
3. Finally, Nature (the investors) chooses a *state of demand* in reaction to the offering price. Demand may depend not only upon the winner's offering price but also upon all of the bids. It is believed by many investment bankers, for example, that the size of the "cover," or difference between the two highest bids, influences the success of the offering. The rationale is that investors are uncertain about the value of the bonds, but that a close bid tends to confirm the judgment of the winning bidder in his pricing of the issue.

At the completion of the third move, each player will receive a prize. His prize will in general depend not only on his own choice but also upon those made by the other players and by Nature. Each losing player at Move 1 gets a prize of 0; we can disregard the costs of preparing the bid, since these are entailed by the decision to play the game in the first place and do not depend upon the final outcome of the game. The value of the winning player's prize depends also upon Nature's reaction. It is even possible that the supposed winner of the first move will end up with a negative prize and hence be worse off than the supposed losers.

It is of interest to note the sequences of moves in the foregoing game. While a player may eventually be required to name a public offering price, at the first

---

[5] If bidders stipulate different coupons, then the comparison should be made in terms of cost of money, as defined by (3-1b). We shall assume throughout this monograph that, when different coupons are stipulated, one coupon rate can be chosen and all costs of money transformed into equivalent bids at this coupon rate, using (3-1b). Since this transformation is monotone, it preserves the order of the bids and hence will not affect the strategic problem.

move he need stipulate only his bid. Should he be the winner at this move, he may take into account information acquired as a result of this move, such as the other bids, before deciding on his second move, the offering price.

3.2.1. *Representation by a Game Tree*

The structure of the bidding game can be clarified with the help of an analytical tool called a *game tree*. A game tree is simply a diagram depicting the choices to be made by each player in a game in their proper sequence. The inspiration for the name should be obvious from Figure 3.1 which represents a relatively simple version of the bidding game. Each node of the tree (heavy dot) corresponds to a move to be made by one of the players or by Nature, and each branch emanating from that node corresponds to one of the choices available to him at that move.

Since each player in the real-world bidding problem has a large, if not infinite, number of choices at each of his moves, a realistic game-tree representation is impractical. The simple version of Figure 3.1 suffices to bring out the essential

Figure 3·1

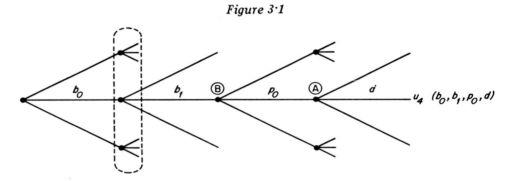

points. Only the generic branches of the tree are represented. It is assumed that there are only two bidders, whom we will designate as Player 0 and Player 1.[6] The game proceeds as follows, reading from left to right in the tree:

1. Player 0 chooses a bid b_0 from a set B_0.
2. Player 1 chooses a bid b_1 from a set B_1. To represent the fact that this choice is made in ignorance of Player 0's choice, the terminal nodes of all branches in B_0 are inclosed within a dotted line; when Player 1 makes his choice, he does not know which of these nodes represents his actual position.[7]

---

[6] In this and the next three chapters, whenever we find it necessary to consider simultaneously the decision problems of several bidders, we will adopt the convention that Player 0 is, so to speak, our "client." That is, we may be concerned with the actions of the other players because of their influence on Player 0's payoff, but we are not seeking to advise these other players what action to take. When necessary to indicate who is to make a given choice, act labels will be subscripted with the player number.

[7] The set of nodes within the dotted line is called an *information set;* see McKinsey, *Introduction to the Theory of Games*, p. 103 ff.

3. Player 0 then chooses an offering price p_0 from a set P_0. This choice becomes operative, of course, only if $b_0 > b_1$, but we will reflect the possibility $b_0 < b_1$ in Player 0's payoff function, to be discussed below. Also, we will not consider Player 1's choice of public offering price since we assume that it will not affect Player 0's payoff function.

4. Nature chooses a market reaction d from a set D. We will assume that the set D is rich enough to include in the description of each $d \, \epsilon \, D$ a statement of the dependence of d on the choices (b_0, b_1, p_0).

5. Finally, Player 0 receives a payoff determined by a function $u_4(\cdot, \cdot, \cdot, \cdot)$ defined on $B_0 \times B_1 \times P_0 \times D$, the set of endpoints of the tree.

The payoff function $u_4(\cdot, \cdot, \cdot, \cdot)$ depends on b_1 in two ways. First, if $b_0 < b_1$ $u_4(b_0, b_1, p_0, d) = 0$ identically in p_0 and d. Second, if $b_0 > b_1$, b_1 will have an indirect effect on u_4 through d. This indirect dependence may, however, be suppressed since it is included in the description of d.

To bring out the details of this payoff structure more clearly, we will first define:

$v_3(b_0, p_0, d) \equiv$ the payoff to Player 0 if he *wins* with a bid of b_0, sets an offering price p_0, and experiences a market reaction d;

and

$$\delta(b_0, b_1) \equiv \begin{cases} 1 & b_0 > b_1 , \\ & \text{if} \\ 0 & b_0 < b_1 . \end{cases}$$

We can then write the payoff function u_4 as

$$u_4(b_0, b_1, p_0, d) = \delta(b_0, b_1)v_3(b_0, p_0, d) .$$

3.2.2. Backwards Induction

We can now indicate how Player 0's decision problem can be solved by working backwards through the tree depicted in Fig. 3.1. The details of the solution will be considered in the next three chapters.

Since the last move—selection of d—belongs to Nature, we will consider $\tilde{d}$ as a random variable; $v_3(b_0, p_0, \tilde{d})$ is then also a random variable. We will assume that Player 0 can assign a (conditional) probability measure $P_{d|b_0,b_1,p_0}$ to the set D, and we will denote the operation of expectation relative to this measure by $E_{d|b_0,b_1,p_0}$. Then Player 0's expected payoff at point A of Fig. 3.1 is given by

$$u_3(b_0, b_1, p_0) = \delta(b_0, b_1)E_{d|b_0,b_1,p_0}v_3(b_0, p_0, \tilde{d})$$
$$\equiv \delta(b_0, b_1)v_2(b_0, b_1, p_0) ,$$

where $v_2(b_0, b_1, p_0)$ is defined implicitly by the identity.

At point B of Fig. 3.1, Player 0 must choose a $p_0 \, \epsilon \, P_0$. We will assume that Player 0 wishes to maximize his expectation $u_3(b_0, b_1, p_0)$; if he chooses according to this principle, his payoff at point B will be given by

$$u_2(b_0, b_1) = \delta(b_0, b_1) \max_{p_0} v_2(b_0, b_1, p_0) \equiv \delta(b_0, b_1)v_1(b_0, b_1) ,$$

where $v_1(b_0, b_1)$ is defined implicitly by the identity and may be interpreted as the value of winning with a bid of b_0 if the opponent bids b_1.

The problem of choosing p_0 will be considered in detail in Chapter 4.

To carry the induction back further through the tree, we need to make some assumption about the choice of Player 1. Two possible approaches will be considered in subsequent chapters.

1. In the Theory of Games, it is assumed that one's opponents are rational decision makers who seek to maximize a known payoff function. This assumption is used to predict how these opponents will behave.

2. Alternatively, Player 0 can treat his opponents as part of Nature, assigning a probability measure P_b for example to the set B_1 of possible bids by Player 1. Player 0 would then choose b_0 to maximize his expectation of $u_2(b_0, b_1)$ against this probability measure.

The game-theoretic approach to the bidding problem will be examined in detail in Chapter 5, and the approach of assigning a probability measure to opponents' bids will be examined in detail in Chapter 6.

CHAPTER 4

The Pricing Decision

As we pointed out in the last chapter, the determination of an optimum bid by a bidding group must depend upon its evaluation of winning the issue, and this evaluation depends in turn upon the public offering price which the group decides to quote. Hence the first step in the analysis of the bidding problem must be the determination of a public offering price. This step will be discussed in the present chapter.

In this chapter we shall continue to treat the bidding group as a single, unitary decision maker whose objective is the maximization of expected monetary value. The internal decision problem of the group is deferred to Chapter 7.

The pricing problem can be analyzed as either a static or a dynamic decision problem.

In the static approach, the bidding group must set a single public offering price to which it will adhere until the issue is sold. The price set will, of course, exert an influence on the time required to sell the issue and thereby on the cost of carrying the inventory of bonds. The problem is to determine the optimal price. This problem is analyzed in Section 4.1. Under particular assumptions as to the relationship of demand to price, solutions are obtained for both the cases of certain and uncertain demand.

In the dynamic approach, on the other hand, the bidding group has the option of changing the offering price periodically. The problem is no longer one of determining the single best price but rather one of determining the best strategy for changing price over time. In the most general formulation of this approach, price changes can be made to depend upon information about demand acquired since the previous change. But even under certainty, when it is impossible by definition to acquire relevant new information, a policy incorporating a variable price may be advisable. These and related points are discussed in Section 4.2.

4.1. Analysis of the Static Pricing Problem

4.1.1. Formulation of the Problem

Demand for a particular bond issue. A decision must be evaluated in the light of its consequences, and the most direct consequence of a particular choice of offering price will be the demand for the bonds.

We will, of course, be interested in the relationship between price and quantity demanded, but we will also be concerned with the effect of demand on inventory, since inventory costs and risks constitute two of the most important factors influencing the relative desirability of various possible prices. Accordingly, we wish to work with a demand function which specifies, for each instant in time and for each possible price, the *rate* at which the bonds will be demanded (i.e., the quantity demanded per unit time).

To formalize the above, let us denote the public offering (as a fraction of par value) by p and the time (measured from the initial public offering of the bonds) by t. The quantity of bonds will be measured in par value. Then the par value which will be demanded at price p in the time interval between t and $(t + dt)$ will be denoted by $d(p, t)\, dt$.

It is reasonable to assume that the market for a particular new bond issue is characterized by imperfect competition. The most important justification for this assumption is that, since the future is uncertain, investors are likely to disagree among themselves on security of the issue; hence there is no objective standard as to what the issue "should" sell at in the market. Accordingly, we will hereafter assume that the rate of demand is a decreasing function of price, i.e., that

$$\frac{\partial}{\partial p}\, d(p, t) < 0, \quad \text{for all} \quad t > 0 \quad \text{and} \quad p > 0 \ . \tag{4-1}$$

Cumulative demand in the interval $(0, T)$ will be represented by

$$D(p, T) \equiv \int_0^T d(p, t)\, dt \ . \tag{4-2}$$

Effect of demand rate on inventory. In addition to its direct effect on the rate of demand, the offering price set by the winning group will exert, through the rate of demand, an indirect effect on the group's inventory of the issue. Denote the total par value of the issue by q; this is then the group's initial inventory at the time it offers the bonds for sale. This initial inventory will be depleted as sales are made, until finally it is reduced to 0.

We will define $\lambda(p)$ implicitly by the following equation:

$$D[p, \lambda(p)] - q = 0 \ . \tag{4-3}$$

Thus $\lambda(p)$ can be interpreted as the time interval necessary to sell the entire issue if the offering price is set at p.

For the time being, we will assume that the bond issue is kept "in syndicate" with the price maintained until the entire issue is sold; later we will take up the more realistic case in which the syndicate agreement might be terminated before all bonds are sold. Under this assumption, the total inventory $I(p, T)$ of bonds in the hands of the syndicate at time T, if the price is set at p, will be given by:

$$I(p, T) = \max\,[q - D(p, T),\, 0] \ . \tag{4-4}$$

Cost of carrying inventory. We will assume that it costs the bidding group \$$k$ to carry \$1 par value of bonds in inventory per unit of time.

As we noted in Chapter 2, it is customary for a bidding group to finance a large part of its inventory of unsold bonds by means of bank loans. On these loans there is, of course, an accounting cost represented by the interest due the bank. For our current purposes, however, we are interested not in this accounting cost but in the opportunity cost to the group represented by the return it could make if it put the same financial resources (including its own equity) to another use. Most investment banking firms, for example, would have the option of diverting their capital to the carrying of inventories of seasoned over-the-counter securities and should do so if the carrying of underwritten inventories does not offer a satisfactory return.

As a rough approximation, k is about .05 per year or .001 per week. This approximation is based on the assumption that the bidding group could invest the funds tied up in an issue in alternative projects with a yield of about 10% per year, against which can be offset the interest accruing on the bonds while they are held at a rate of 4% to 5% per year. On a \$25 million issue, the total cost of carrying inventory for one week would thus be on the order of \$25,000. This cost may be compared with the group's spread on the issue, which will be on the order of 0.75% of par value or \$187,500. Since over half of this spread must normally go for selling commissions and other nonfinancial costs, it is evident that a group cannot carry all of an issue very long in inventory and still earn a profit.

The total cost $K(p)$ of carrying the inventory of bonds until sold is, therefore,

$$K(p) \equiv k \int_0^{\lambda(p)} I(p, T) \, dT$$

$$= kq\lambda(p) - k \int_0^{\lambda(p)} D(p, T) \, dT \;, \tag{4-5}$$

with the right-hand side resulting from substitution of (4-4).

Net return. We will define the net return $R(p)$ from the sale of the bond issue as the total proceeds from the sale less the inventory carrying costs, i.e.,

$$R(p) \equiv pq - K(p)$$

$$= pq - kq\lambda(p) + k \int_0^{\lambda(p)} D(p, T) \, dT \;. \tag{4-6}$$

Inasmuch as the entire revenue pq will not be received immediately, it might be argued that the revenue ought to be discounted. Since, however, we have already reflected the opportunity cost of capital to the bidder in the inventory cost parameter k, discounting revenue would amount to double-counting. In Sec. 4.2, on the other hand, we will present a model in which future revenue is discounted but no allowance is made for inventory carrying cost. Either method accomplishes the same result; the choice in this case is a matter of convenience.

In (4-6) we ignore certain other costs associated with an underwriting (selling concessions, legal and administrative costs, etc.), since these costs do not depend upon p and hence will not affect the choice of a best p. These costs are, of course, relevant to other decisions, such as whether and how much to bid on the issue, and we will return to them in Chapters 5 and 6. In the definition we also make no explicit mention of the possible dependence of net return on the "cover," or difference between the winning bid and the second best bid. However, we can interpret the demand function $d(p, t)$ to reflect this dependence.

41

4.1.2. Optimum Price Under Certainty

If there is no uncertainty about demand, the objective of a winning bidder will be to set the public offering price p such as to maximize $R(p)$. In this section we will assume that the demand function has a continuous derivative with respect to p and we will derive the first-order conditions for this maximization for the general demand function $d(p, t)$ and for two successively more special cases.

General case. To obtain the first-order condition for a maximum net return, we differentiate (4-6) with respect to p and set the result equal to zero:

$$R'(p) = q - kq\lambda'(p) + k \left[\int_0^{\lambda(p)} \frac{\partial}{\partial p} D(p, T) \, dT + q\lambda'(p) \right]$$

$$= q + k \int_0^{\lambda(p)} \int_0^T \frac{\partial}{\partial p} d(p, t) \, dt \, dT \qquad (4\text{-}7)$$

$$= 0 \; .$$

Special case I. To be able to make more specific observations on optimal pricing, we will examine the special case where the demand function remains constant over time; i.e., we will assume that $d(p, t) = d(p)$ for all t, at least in the interval 0 to $\lambda(p)$. In this case, we have

$$D(p, T) = \int_0^T d(p) \, dt = Td(p) \; . \qquad (4\text{-}8)$$

It then follows from (4-3) that

$$\lambda(p) = q/d(p) \; . \qquad (4\text{-}9)$$

Substituting (4-8) and (4-9) into the net return function (4-6) and integrating out T, we obtain

$$R(p) = pq - kq^2/2d(p) \; . \qquad (4\text{-}10)$$

By differentiating (4-10) with respect to p [or by substituting (4-8) and (4-9) into (4-7)], we obtain as the first order condition for a maximum:

$$R'(p) = q + kq^2 d'(p)/2[d(p)]^2 = 0 \; . \qquad (4\text{-}11)$$

We can give the following economic interpretation to (4-11). Multiply through by $pd(p)$, i.e., the rate at which gross revenue is earned per unit of time. Upon rearrangement of terms and simplification this results in the condition

$$\frac{pd'(p)}{d(p)} = -\frac{2}{kq} pd(p) \; . \qquad (4\text{-}12)$$

The left-hand side of (4-12) is, by definition, the price elasticity of demand. At optimality, therefore, price elasticity must be a multiple of the rate at which gross revenue is earned.

Special case II. Let us assume that there is a public offering price p_c such that $\lambda(p_c) = 0$; that is, if the bonds are offered at p_c, they will be sold instantaneously. On the other hand, for $p > p_c$ we will assume that $\lambda(p) > 0$.

It also seems reasonable to assume that $\lambda(p)$ is in some way related to the difference $(p - p_c)$. The simplest such relationship would be linear; that is, that the time required to sell the issue is proportional to the difference $(p - p_c)$. Somewhat more interesting results will be obtained, however, if we postulate the more general relationship

$$\lambda(p) = \alpha(p - p_c)^\beta \ , \quad p \geq p_c \ , \quad \alpha > 0 \ , \quad \beta > 1 \ . \tag{4-13}$$

The expression (4-13) implies that not only will the length of time required to sell the issue increase with an increase in price above p_c but that this increase will be more than proportional.

Equation (4-13), taken with (4-9), implies that the demand function is

$$d(p) = q/\alpha(p - p_c)^\beta \quad \text{for} \quad p > p_c \ , \quad \alpha > 0 \ , \quad \beta > 1 \ ; \tag{4-14}$$

and, substituting (4-14) into (4-10), that the net return is

$$R(p) = pq - [kq\alpha(p - p_c)^\beta]/2 \ . \tag{4-15}$$

To determine the optimum price, we can either differentiate (4-15) directly or else differentiate (4-14) and then use (4-11). Following the latter course, we find first that

$$d'(p) = - \ \beta q/\alpha(p - p_c)^{\beta+1},$$

which shows that (4-14) is consistent with (4-1). We can then calculate that

$$d'(p)/[d(p)]^2 = - \ \alpha\beta(p - p_c)^{\beta-1}/q \ .$$

Substituting this last result into (4-11) yields as the condition for the optimal price p^*

$$p^* = p_c + (2/k\alpha\beta)^{1/(\beta-1)} \ . \tag{4-16}$$

Since $R''(p) = -\tfrac{1}{2}[kq\alpha\beta(\beta - 1)(p - p_c)^{\beta-2}]$ and since k, q, α, β are all positive, with $\beta > 1$, the second-order condition for a maximum is also satisfied at p^*.

We can interpret $(2/k\alpha\beta)^{1/(\beta-1)}$ as the *optimum amount of "overpricing"* relative to the price which would clear the market instantly. It is a decreasing function of each of the three parameters k, α, and β.

Thus, the optimum amount of overpricing is *reduced* if: (a) inventory carrying costs (k) are increased; (b) the market reaction rate to overpricing (α) is increased; or (c) the severity of the market reaction (β) is increased. (We will discuss the parameters α and k further in Sec. 4.1.5).

In Sec. 4.1.3, we will take up the question of determining p^* under uncertainty regarding p_c (i.e., when only a probability distribution of p_c, possibly subjective, is known). It will turn out that analysis of the pricing problem under uncertainty is especially convenient when $\beta = 2$; i.e., when the time required to sell the issue, $\lambda(p)$, is quadratic in the unknown parameter p_c. In this case, by specializing (4-16), we have

$$p^* = p_c + \frac{1}{k\alpha} \ , \quad \text{if} \quad \beta = 2 \ . \tag{4-16'}$$

Substituting (4-16') into (4-15), we find that the maximum net revenue with $\beta = 2$ is

$$R(p^*) = q \left(p_c + \frac{1}{2k\alpha} \right) \cdot \tag{4-17}$$

4.1.3. Optimum Price Under Uncertainty with Stationary Demand

In this analysis we will continue to assume that the demand process is characterized by (4-13), except that now $\lambda(p)$ will be unknown. Initially we will assume that all the uncertainty about $\lambda(p)$ resides in p_c; α will be assumed known with certainty, and we will consider only the case $\beta = 2$. The assumption that α is known amounts to saying that the bidding group does not know the price necessary to sell the issue instantaneously, but it does know the nature of the market's reaction to a deviation from this price. (We will consider uncertainty about α briefly at the end of this section.)

On the assumption that the group's objective is to maximize expected monetary value, it seeks to maximize the expectation of (4-15), or

$$\mathrm{E}[R(p)] = pq - \tfrac{1}{2}(kq\alpha\mathrm{E}[(p - \tilde{p}_c)^2]) \;, \tag{4-18}$$

where the notation $\tilde{p}_c$ is used to indicate that $\tilde{p}_c$ is a random variable. Let us define $\overline{p}_c = \mathrm{E}(\tilde{p}_c)$, $\breve{p}_c = \mathrm{E}[(\tilde{p}_0 - \overline{p}_c)^2]$. Then since

$$\mathrm{E}[(p - \tilde{p}_c)^2] = \mathrm{E}\{[(p - \overline{p}_c) + (\overline{p}_c - \tilde{p}_c)]^2\}$$
$$= (p - \overline{p}_c)^2 + \breve{p}_c \;.$$

we have

$$\mathrm{E}[R(p)] = q\left[p - \frac{k\alpha}{2}(p - \overline{p}_c)^2 - \frac{k\alpha\breve{p}_c}{2} \right]. \tag{4-19}$$

The last term inside the brackets on the right-hand side of (4-19) does not involve p and hence will not influence the determination of the optimum price p^*. If we compare the remainder of the left-hand side of (4-19) with (4-15), we see that, after making the substitution $\beta = 2$, they are identical except that the expectation of p_c appears in (4-19) in place of p_c itself. Thus we can conclude, by comparison with (4-16), that

$$p^* = \overline{p}_c + 1/k\alpha \;, \tag{4-20}$$

and that the maximum expected net return

$$\mathrm{E}[R(p^*)] = q(\overline{p}_c + 1/2k\alpha - k\alpha\breve{p}_c/2) \;. \tag{4-21}$$

Some comment on these last two results is in order. For purposes of determining the optimum price under uncertainty, we see that the expected value $\overline{p}_c$ of the market-clearing price is a certainty equivalent; no other information about the probability distribution of $\tilde{p}_c$ is required. This result is a consequence of the fact that the criterion function (4-19) is quadratic in p and $\tilde{p}_c$.[1]

When we come to the maximum expected net return, however, $\overline{p}_c$ is no longer sufficient; $\mathrm{E}[R(p^*)]$ depends also on $\breve{p}_c$. This is of some importance, since $\mathrm{E}[R(p^*)]$, when adjusted for selling and other expenses not dependent on p, is the value of winning the bid and hence feeds back on the choice of an optimal bid. We find, therefore, that the degree of a group's uncertainty about the demand parameter $\tilde{p}_c$, as reflected in its variance $\breve{p}_c$, will have an effect on its choice of an overall strategy

---

[1] Cf. Raiffa and Schlaifer, *Applied Statistical Decision Theory*, p. 188.

even on the assumption that the group objective is the maximization of monetary expected value.

Up to this point we have treated α as known with certainty. Since α enters into (4-18) linearly, if it is unknown and if we can assume that it is uncorrelated with $\tilde{p}_c$, then its expected value may be used as a certainty equivalent in determining p^* and $\mathrm{E}[R(p^*)]$. (The same comment is true of k.) There is nonetheless interest in examining the sensitivity of maximum net return to errors in estimating α since this examination bears on the question of whether it is worthwhile to obtain additional information about α before taking terminal action.

Let $\hat{\alpha}$ be an estimate of α used in (4-20) to determine optimum price, and let $\hat{p}$ be the (estimated) optimum price so determined. The expected net revenue at this price will be

$$\mathrm{E}[R(\hat{p})] = q[\bar{p}_c + (2 - \alpha/\hat{\alpha})/2k\hat{\alpha} - k\alpha\check{p}_c/2] \ . \tag{4-22}$$

As a measure of the sensitivity of the pricing decision to a misestimate of α, we may take

$$\frac{\mathrm{E}[R(p^*)] - \mathrm{E}[R(\hat{p})]}{q} = \frac{1}{2k\alpha} - \frac{2 - \alpha/\hat{\alpha}}{2k\alpha}$$

$$= \frac{1}{2k\alpha} \left(\frac{\alpha - \hat{\alpha}}{\hat{\alpha}}\right)^2 \ . \tag{4-23}$$

The loss in expected net revenue, therefore, is proportional to the squared proportional error for fixed α.

In Sec. 4.1.4, we will discuss briefly the problem of estimating α. Suffice it to say now that an order-of-magnitude estimate of the ratio $\dfrac{1}{2k\alpha}$ is .005. Now suppose that $(\alpha - \hat{\alpha})/\hat{\alpha} = .2$; that is, the true value of α is either 20% larger or smaller than the estimate $\hat{\alpha}$. Then, by (4-23)

$$\frac{\mathrm{E}[R(p^*)] - \mathrm{E}[R(\hat{p})]}{q} = (.005)(.2)^2 = .0002 \ .$$

This error is in units of dollars per dollar of par value. It is evidently negligible, amounting to only 20¢ per $1,000 bond. For this reason, we can feel justified in ignoring uncertainty regarding α.

4.1.4. Application of the Model

Most of the specific results of the last section depend, of course, on the assumption that the demand process is described by (4-14), as further specialized in some instances to the case $\beta = 2$. We will now examine some of the implications which follow from this assumption.

If we set $\beta = 2$, the demand function (4-14) has two free parameters, α and p_c. Intuitively, the parameter p_c can be taken to represent a characteristic of the particular issue being sold; it is an indicator of where the issue "stands" in the market at the time issuance. Presumably, therefore, p_c must be estimated by a security analysis combined with a cross-sectional comparison with other bond issues.

45

The parameter α, on the other hand, appears to be representative of a characteristic of the bond market generally. More specifically, it is a measure of the imperfection of the market. If α is high, the market will react quite sharply to deviations from the "ideal" price p_c, and we have a condition close to pure competition. If α is low, moderate overpricing will not have a substantial effect on the rate of demand.

If this interpretation of α is valid, then it might be reasonable to expect α to remain fairly stable over time and there might be some hope of estimating it statistically. While this estimation has not been attempted in this monograph, it remains an intriguing possibility for further research.

We can arrive at a rough order-of-magnitude estimate of α by considering how investment bankers actually price issues. As we pointed out in Chapter 2, the winning group will usually try to move the issue within a relatively short period of time, say a week or about .02 years. Assuming that this is an optimal policy and that $\beta = 2$, this implies that

$$\lambda(p^*) = \alpha(p^* - p_c)^2 = .02 ,$$

with time measured in years. From (4-16) we determine that $(p^* - p_c) = 1/k\alpha$, so that we must have

$$\frac{1}{\alpha k^2} = .02 \quad \text{or} \quad \alpha = \frac{50}{k^2} .$$

We previously gave an order-of-magnitude estimate of .05 for k, with time measured in years. Therefore, assuming optimal pricing by investment bankers, they are behaving as if

$$\alpha = \frac{50}{(.05)^2} = 20,000 .$$

With this estimate of α, a bond issue overpriced by .01 of par value would require

$$\lambda(p_c + .01) = (20,000)(.01)^2 = 2 \text{ years}$$

to dispose of; since an overpricing of this magnitude amounts to a reduction of only about .03% in the yield to the buyers, this would seem to indicate that the bankers are operating on the basis of an excessively high estimate of α. In view of the many assumptions and estimates underlying the last calculation, however, perhaps not too much credence should be placed in it. The calculation omits, for example, the possibility that an initially unfavorable demand rate will have an unfavorable effect on subsequent demand, i.e., that $\frac{\partial}{\partial t} d(p, t)$ may be an increasing function of $d(p, t)$. This possibility would reduce the amount of overpricing at the optimum.

Another approach to an order-of-magnitude estimate of α, subject to the same objections just raised, would reverse the process used above. That is, we would estimate directly the effect on $\lambda(p_c + \delta)$ of a given δ, and, then, using (4-13), solve for δ. The writer would consider .2 year (about ten weeks) a reasonable order-of-magnitude estimate of the time required to dispose of an issue overpriced by .01; that is,

$$\lambda(p_c + .01) = \alpha(.01)^2 = .2 .$$

From this, we can determine that

$$\alpha = \frac{.2}{.0001} = 2{,}000 \ ,$$

and that

$$p^* = p_c + \frac{1}{(2)(.05)(2{,}000)}$$
$$= p_c + .005 \ ;$$

i.e., that the optimum amount of overpricing is on the order of .005 of par value, or between .01% and .02% in yield to the buyer. We can apply (4-23) to determine the degree of non-optimality of the bankers' behavior, assuming that the true α is near 2,000. Since they appear to be acting on the basis of an estimate $\alpha = 20{,}000$, we can calculate that $(\alpha - \hat{\alpha})/\hat{\alpha} = -.9$, and therefore that

$$\frac{E[R(p^*)] - E[R(\hat{p})]}{q} = (.005)(.81) = .00405 \ .$$

This difference amounts to \$4.05 per \$1,000 bond, a substantial sum when it is considered that the spread is likely to be on the order of \$7.50 per bond.

4.2. Analysis of the Dynamic Pricing Problem

4.2.1. Single-Stage Pricing Problem with a Boundary Condition

As a preliminary to the full multistage analysis of the pricing problem later in this section, we will first consider the following modification of the single-stage problem: At the beginning of a fixed interval of time, the bidding group offers a bond issue at price p. A certain quantity, depending upon the price, is sold at this price during the interval. The bonds remaining at the end of the interval, if any, are assigned a value to the group.

This formulation of the pricing problem, it will be observed, closely parallels the procedure actually employed by a winning syndicate, as described in Chapter 2. The syndicate agreement has a fixed life and, while the agreement may be extended, usually the bonds remaining unsold when the agreement is terminated are disposed of on a different basis from those sold during the life of the agreement.

We will formalize this analysis in the following way. A total par value of q is to be sold. At the beginning of the selling period, the group sets an offering price p. At this price, a quantity of bonds $d(p)$ is demanded and a quantity $h(p)$ is sold (the quantity is measured in par value). Since sales cannot exceed the quantity available,

$$h(p) \equiv \min\,[q,\,d(p)] \ . \tag{4-24}$$

The net revenue to the group from sales made during the selling period is $R[h(p)]$. If the entire par value of q is not sold in the first period, the balance carried over to the next period has a value to the group of $v[q - h(p)]$. The total return S which the group seeks to maximize is thus

47

$$S = R[h(p)] + v[q - h(p)] . \qquad (4\text{-}25)$$

We will examine only the case of decreasing marginal returns; that is, we will assume both that $R''(x) < 0$ and that $v''(x) < 0$.

Let us first look at the maximization of S under the assumption that $h(p) = d(p)$, ignoring the constraint on first-period sales implied by (4-24). This is a relatively simple matter; the maximum return is achieved when $h = d(p)$ satisfies

$$R'(h) = v'(q - h) , \qquad (4\text{-}26)$$

i.e., when the marginal return in the two periods is equal. The optimum price p^* can then be found by finding the solution of (4-26), say h^*, and then solving $h^* = d(p^*)$ for p^*.

If the solution of (4-26) also satisfies (4-24), then the constrained maximum of S is the same as the unconstrained maximum and the price determined as in the preceding paragraph is also the optimum in the constrained problem. If, on the other hand, the solution of (4-26) fails to satisfy (4-24), then the optimum price in the constrained problem is found by solving $q = d(p^*)$ for p^*. That is, the price found according to the preceding paragraph is adjusted until the quantity demanded is equal to the fixed supply. This conclusion follows from the assumptions that $R''(x) < 0$ and $v''(x) < 0$; these assumptions insure that for $h < h^*$, $R'(h) > v'(q - h)$, so that it is unprofitable to shift any more sales from period 1 to period 2 than is absolutely necessary to meet condition (4-24).

Under uncertainty, the objective is the maximization of the expected value of (4-25). The solution becomes somewhat more involved, however, since under uncertainty the quantity demanded at a given price is a random variable. This fact affects the treatment both of the marginal condition (4-26) and of the boundary condition (4-24). It will accordingly be more convenient to introduce uncertainty after we have unveiled the full apparatus for dealing with the dynamic pricing problem.

4.2.2. *Multistage Pricing Problem with Stationary Demand*

Thus far in this chapter we have assumed that once a bidding group decided on a public offering price it would maintain it either until all the bonds were sold (Sec. 4.1) or until the termination of the syndicate agreement (Sec. 4.2.1). It is true that in Sec. 4.2.1 the assignment of a different value to unsold bonds than to bonds sold at the original offering price may be interpreted to include the possibility of a price change at the end of period 1. However, no explicit attention was given to the problem of determining a *best* price for period 2.

We will now begin consideration of the case in which the bidding group has the option of changing the public offering price at discrete points in time, for instance daily. The interval between the points at which price changes may be made will be taken as the unit of measure of time. We will at first consider the case in which the number of intervals over which the bonds will be offered is finite; any bonds remaining unsold at the end of the last interval will be assigned a value.

We will assume at this point that the quantity demanded in any period will be a known function of the price and that this function will be the same in all periods. Generalization to the case of unknown demand will be discussed in Sec. 4.2.3.

Let q_t be the quantity of bonds available for sale by the group with t periods remaining until the termination of the offering. At the beginning of the period, the group sets an offering price p_t. At this price, a quantity of bonds $d(p_t)$ is demanded and a quantity $h(p_t)$ sold. Since sales in any period cannot exceed the quantity available at the beginning of the period,

$$h_t(p_t) \equiv \min \left[q_t, d(p_t) \right] . \tag{4-27}$$

The inventory carried over into the succeeding period is given by

$$q_{t-1} = q_t - h_t(p_t) . \tag{4-28}$$

The net revenue to the group from sales made during the period will be represented by $R[h_t(p_t)]$. The value of any bonds remaining unsold at the termination of the offering will be $v_0(q_0)$.

As in Sec. 4.1, there will be a charge for carrying inventories of unsold bonds, for which we will account by discounting the revenue to be received one period hence by a factor ρ, where $0 < \rho < 1$.

Suppose that the offering period is to extend over T periods in all, and that the par value of the issue is $q = q_T$. Then the bidding group seeks to choose $p_T, p_{T-1}, \cdots, p_1$, so as to maximize

$$S = \sum_{i=0}^{T-1} \rho^i R[h_{T-i}(p_{T-i})] + \rho^T v_0 \left[q - \sum_{i=0}^{T-1} h_{T-i}(p_{T-i}) \right] . \tag{4-29}$$

We will assume that marginal return is decreasing in all periods; i.e., that $R''(x) < 0$ and that $v_0''(x) < 0$.

As in Sec. 4.2.1, let us look first at the maximization of S under the assumption that $h_t(p_t) = d(p_t)$, ignoring the constraint implied by (4-27). The solution in this case is analogous to that of Sec. 4.2.1: the *discounted marginal return must be equal in all periods*, including the post-termination period. That is, we must have

$$\rho^i R'[h_{T-i}(p_{T-i})] = \rho^T v_0' \left[q - \sum_{i=0}^{T-1} h_{T-i}(p_{T-1}) \right] = \text{constant}, \qquad \text{all } i < T . \tag{4-30}$$

If the sequence $h_T(p_T), h_{T-1}(p_{T-1}), \cdots, h_1(p_1)$ obtained by solving (4-30) also satisfies (4-27), then it is the solution to the constrained maximization problem. The sequence of optimal prices, $p_T^*, p_{T-1}^*, \cdots, p_1^*$, can be obtained by solving

$$d(p_t^*) = s(p_t^*) , \quad \text{for} \quad t = 1, 2, \cdots, T .$$

This solution permits us to draw an interesting conclusion regarding the nature of the optimum policy under constant demand. Suppose that (4-30) gives a solution of the constrained maximization problem and that $v_0'(x) \geq 0$ for all x. This last assumption should generally be true, since the group can always insure a marginal return of 0 in the last period by simply destroying the remaining bonds. Then one of the following will be true:

(a) The discounted marginal return will be 0 in all periods. That is, the group acts to maximize total revenue on a period-by-period basis. Under constant demand, this implies that the public offering price must be the same in all periods.

(b) The discounted marginal revenue will be positive (and non-zero) in all periods. But if the *discounted* marginal revenue is the same in all periods, then the *undiscounted* marginal revenue must increase with time. Under constant demand with decreasing marginal revenue, this implies that the optimal price also increases with time, i.e.,

$$p_T^* < p_{T-1}^* < \cdots < p_1^* .$$

The foregoing conclusions depend, of course, upon the assumption that the solution to (4-30) also satisfies (4-27). If this condition is not satisfied, then it is no longer necessarily true that discounted marginal revenue is equal in *all* periods. A solution to the problem can still be obtained, however, by employing the functional equation technique of dynamic programming.

We can formulate the problem in dynamic programming terms in the following way. Let $v_t(q_t)$ be the discounted net return available over t intervals from the sale of bonds if the present inventory is q_t and if an optimal pricing policy is followed. We can then write the following recursive relation for $v_t(q_t)$.

$$v_t(q_t) = \max_{0 \leq h_t \leq q_t} [R(h_t) + \rho v_{t-1}(q_t - h_t)] ; \tag{4-31}$$

we will let $v_t(0) = 0$ for all t.

The relation (4-31) is an application of the Principle of Optimality of dynamic programming;[2] a policy which is optimal must be optimal over the next t intervals as well as in the next interval itself.

We can solve (4-31) for the optimal policy as follows. First $v_0(q_0)$ must be specified as a boundary condition; we will continue to assume that $v_0''(q_0) < 0$. We then find $v_1(q_1)$ recursively:

$$v_1(q_1) = \max_{0 \leq h_1 \leq q_1} [R(h_1) + \rho v_0(q_1 - h_1)] . \tag{4-32}$$

With the exception of the discount factor ρ, the decision problem described by (4-32) is identical with the single-period problem discussed in Sec. 4.2.1. We can conclude, therefore, that the solution is of the following form: The optimal one-period price p_1^* is the solution of

$$R[d(p_1)] = \rho v_0'[q_1 - d(p_1)] ,$$

provided that $d(p_1^*) \leq q_1$. If not, p_1^* is the solution of

$$q_1 = d(p_1) .$$

Since p_1^* depends upon the beginning-of-interval inventory q_1, we will emphasize this dependence by using the notation $p_1^*(q_1)$.

Once $p_1^*(q_1)$ has been determined, we can evaluate $v_1(q_1)$. Having done so, we then proceed to find $p_2(q_2)$ and $v_2(q_2)$, and so on recursively until the optimal

---

[2] See R. Bellman, *Dynamic Programming*, p. 83.

price for the initial interval p_T has been obtained. The existence and uniqueness of a solution are guaranteed[3] by the concavity of $R(x)$ and $v_0(x)$.

4.2.3. *Multistage Pricing Problem Under Uncertainty*

Under uncertainty, the exact quantity which will be demanded at a given price is a random variable. The problem can be formulated as follows. We will now let $v_t(q_t)$ be the maximum *expected* net return from a selling period of t intervals starting with an initial inventory of q_t. The probability that the quantity of bonds demanded will be between h and $h + dh$, given that the public offering price is p, will be denoted by $f(h; p)dh$. The cumulative probability that the quantity demanded will be greater than q will be denoted by $G(q; p)$. All other notation will be as in the preceding section.

We can then write the following recursive relation for $v_t(q_t)$:

$$v_t(q_t) = \max_{p_t \geq 0} \left[\int_0^q \left[R(h_t) + \rho v_{t-1}(q_t - h_t) \right] f(h_t; p_t) \, dh_t + R(q_t) G(q_t; p_t) \right] ; \quad (4\text{-}33)$$

as before, we will assume that $v_t(0) = 0$ for all t.

The functional equation (4-33) may be solved in the same manner as (4-32). If $v_0(q_0)$ is given, we use it to find the optimum pricing policy p_1^* for the last period. This permits us to evaluate $v_1(q_1)$ and $p_2^*(q_2)$, and so on.

A special case of (4-33) has been formulated by Darling and is the basis for a problem set in Bellman.[4] Darling assumes that demand in any period can be characterized by a Bernoulli process in which the probability that any one item is demanded depends upon price.

An obvious generalization of (4-33) would be to permit the probability distribution of demand to vary from period to period. A Bayes model, in which the distribution depended on actual demand in earlier periods, would be appropriate. Assessment of the conditional distributions might, however, pose an exceptionally difficult problem.

4.2.4. *Application of the Dynamic Models*

The most difficult feature in the practical application of the dynamic models discussed in this section would undoubtedly be the estimation of the demand functions or probability distributions required, particularly if the assumption of stationarity proves untenable. The development of practical estimation procedures is a fruitful area for further research.

It may not always be possible to find analytical solutions to the dynamic models, but with the existence of high-speed computers this is not always of practical consequence. Computational techniques for dealing with dynamic programming problems are discussed in a recent work by Bellman and Dreyfus.[5]

---

[3] The proof is a special case of a theorem in *ibid.*, p. 119. The optimality conditions can also be derived by application of the Kuhn-Tucker conditions for concave programming; see Dorfman *et al.*, *Linear Programming and Economic Analysis*, pp. 189–201.

[4] *Op. cit.*, p. 334.

[5] Bellman and Dreyfus, *Applied Dynamic Programming*.

CHAPTER 5

The Bidding Decision: Game-Theoretic Analysis

In Section 3.2.2 two possible analytical approaches to the determination of a bid price were briefly discussed. In this chapter, we will consider in detail the first of these approaches, the Theory of Games. In Chapter 6 the alternative approach, based on Bayesian decision theory, will be presented.

The Theory of Games is concerned with the decision problems of two or more decision makers whose strategies interact in determining the final payoffs. A brief introduction to the basic concepts of game theory is given in the first section of this chapter. In Section 5.2 the bidding problem is formulated as a game which is to be played once and only once. It is somewhat surprising to note that the "solution" to this game does not depend on the number of bidders so long as this number is at least two.

In Section 5.3 the analysis is extended to the case in which the bidding is to be repeated indefinitely on successive issues but with interim payoffs to the players at each bid. Under some assumptions, this form of the game will result in higher payoffs per trial to the players than the single-trial game.

Finally, in Section 5.4 we draw some conclusions regarding the implications, both normative and descriptive, of the game-theoretic analysis for real-world problems.

5.1. Basic Concepts of the Theory of Games

5.1.1. Strategies, Payoffs, and Objectives

An n-person game can be characterized by specifying:

1. A strategy set $S_i = \{s_i\}$ for each of the players in the game. Player i selects a strategy s_i from some domain S_i; and
2. A real-valued payoff function M_i for each of the players defined on the product set $\Pi_i S_i$.

As in Section 3.2, we will occasionally find it convenient to distinguish one of the players as the "client" for our analysis; this player will be designated by the subscript 0. Therefore the subscripts in statements (1) and (2) above range over the index set $\{0, 1, \cdots, n-1\}$. This convention is nonstandard; in the literature of game theory it is customary to use the index 0 to distinguish "Nature" considered as a player. In this and the next chapter, however, we shall not find it necessary to refer to possible "states of nature."

Therefore, the value $M_i(s_0, \cdots, s_i, \cdots, s_{n-1})$ is the payoff to Player i if the strategies $s_0, \cdots, s_i, \cdots, s_{n-1}$ are chosen by the respective players.

Strategies. The characterization of a game just discussed, in which each player is restricted to the choice of a single strategy, might appear not to apply to games played sequentially, in which each player might choose an act at one or more different "moves" during the play of the game. This appearance would be incorrect, however, since such a game can always be reduced to the form in which each player may make only a single choice in the following way: The sequential game is first laid out in the form of a tree diagram, as in Figure 3.1. The nodes of the tree are then partitioned into mutually exclusive and collectively exhaustive *information sets*, each such set belonging to a particular player and representing the state of that player's information at the time he must make the choice called for at a node included in the information set. That is, the player is informed at any given move of the information set he is in but not of which node he is at (unless, of course, the set contains only one node).[1]

A *pure strategy* s'_i for Player i may then be defined as a function defined for each information set belonging to Player i and whose value for each such set is one of the alternatives there available to Player i.[2] The set of Player i's pure strategies will be called S'_i. Every possible play of the sequential game can then be represented by the assumption that each player chooses one and only one strategy from his set of pure strategies.

For reasons to appear subsequently, however, we shall hereafter assume that the set S_i from which Player i selects his strategy is *not* the set S'_i of his pure strategies but rather the set of all probability measures over the measurable subsets of S'_i. Each element s_i of the set so defined is called a *mixed strategy*. Since the set S_i includes, among others, those probability measures which assign their entire mass to a single element of S'_i, the set S'_i is essentially equivalent to a proper subset of S_i. Thus Player i can always choose what amounts to a pure strategy from S_i by selecting an s_i which corresponds to an element of S'_i. If, on the other hand, he chooses an s_i which does *not* correspond to an element of S'_i, then his pure strategy which is actually followed in the play of the game will be chosen by a random device.

Payoff and objectives. The payoff functions M_i are defined only on the product set $\Pi_i S_i$, but the *terminal payoff* to each player may depend also on moves made by Nature, or chance moves. In the Theory of Games, it is assumed that a probability measure is assigned to the set of possible states of Nature and that the payoff functions M_i are obtained from the terminal payoff functions by expectation with respect to this measure.

It is also assumed that the objective of each player (other than Nature) is to maximize the expected value of his payoff function.

[1] A formal characterization of information sets may be found in McKinsey, *Introduction to the Theory of Games*, p. 119.
[2] *Ibid.*, p. 120.

These assumptions about the payoff functions are valid if and only if the preferences of each player satisfy certain axioms of rational decision making under uncertainty. Various versions of this axiom system may be found in published sources.[3]

Knowledge of players. Each player is assumed to be capable of doing a complete analysis not only of his own decision problem but also of those of all of his opponents. This implies that each player is familiar with *all* the strategy sets S_i and with *all* the payoff functions M_i. This assumption of symmetric rationality is perhaps the key distinguishing feature of the Theory of Games.

5.1.2. Classification of Games

The scheme of classification of games originally proposed by von Neumann and Morgenstern[4] and subsequently followed in much of the literature of game theory is this: We first consider whether the sum of all the payoffs received by the players in the game is identically zero, i.e., whether

$$\sum_{i=0}^{n-1} M_i(s_0, \cdots, s_i, \cdots, s_{n-1}) = 0 \qquad \text{all } s_i, \text{ all } i . \tag{5-1}$$

If (5-1) is satisfied, then the game is called *zero sum*. If not, the game is *non-zero sum*.[5] Games are then further classified by von Neumann and Morgenstern as either 2-person or n-person $(n > 2)$.

Based on this classification, the program laid out by von Neumann and Morgenstern for "solving" games called first for reducing each n-person non-zero-sum game to an $(n + 1)$-person zero-sum game through the introduction of a fictitious player whose payoff is the negative of the sum of the other players' payoffs. Each n-person zero-sum game is reduced to a 2-person zero-sum game in which the two "players" are coalitions of the n players in the original game. Thus, the theory of 2-person zero-sum games (which is to be discussed in Sec. 5.1.4 below) was to be the foundation of the entire theory of games.

This effort to construct the entire edifice on the 2-person zero-sum foundation has not proven entirely satisfactory.[6] An alternative approach, originating with John Nash,[7] relies on a different classification scheme. First, we may classify games as *strictly competitive* or *non-strictly competitive*. In a strictly competitive game, no coalition of two or more players is able, by coordination of strategies, to obtain a payoff which is greater than the sum of the payoffs the players could achieve acting singly. All other games, in which an opportunity exists to form profitable coalitions, are non-strictly competitive. All 2-person zero-sum[8] games

---

[3] For example, Luce and Raiffa, *Games and Decisions*, Chapter 2.

[4] *Theory of Games and Economic Behavior*, pp. 46–47.

[5] If a constant is subtracted from the payoff of one of the players, his strategic problem is not affected, since the ordering of his strategies in terms of expected payoff does not change. Hence, any game in which the payoff sum is a constant unequal to zero can always be reduced to a strategically equivalent zero-sum game.

[6] A critique of game theory may be found in Luce and Raiffa, *op. cit.*

[7] "Non-cooperative games," *Annals of Mathematics*, Vol. 54 (1951), pp. 286–295.

[8] Or constant sum; see note 5.

are strictly competitive, but not all strictly competitive games are either 2-person or zero-sum.

In the Nash theory, games are further classified according to whether the rules of the game permit coalitions to be formed. If coalitions are permissible, the game is *cooperative*; if they are forbidden, it is *non-cooperative*. We can (and will) consider all strictly competitive games to be non-cooperative, since, regardless of the rules of the game, there can be no profit to the players in forming coalitions.

Nash provides a solution theory for non-cooperative (including strictly competitive) games which is a natural generalization of the von Neumann theory for 2-person zero-sum games. This theory will be discussed in the next section, and its specialization to the 2-person zero-sum case in the section following that. Nash proposes that each cooperative game be embedded in a non-cooperative game in which the negotiations leading to formation of coalitions are represented by moves; then his non-cooperative solution theory would apply.

The Nash program for dealing with cooperative games, like the von Neumann-Morgenstern program for other than 2-person zero-sum games, is not without its difficulties.[9] These need not concern us in this chapter, however, since the bidding problem is, by its rules, a non-cooperative game. In the remainder of this chapter, therefore, we will restrict our attention to the non-cooperative case.

5.1.3. Equilibrium Points of Non-Cooperative Games

Suppose that a satisfactory theory exists of how to play the game described in Sec. 5.1.1. By the assumptions of mutual rationality and knowledge, we may assume that each of the players is aware of this theory and is able to apply it to determine his "best" strategy. These putative "best" strategies may be identified with a point $(s_0^*, s_1^*, \cdots, s_{n-1}^*)$ in the product set $\Pi_i S_i$.

Consider now Player 0. By assumption, Player 0 can analyze the decision problems of all of his opponents and can determine that their "best" strategies are $s_1^*, \cdots, s_{n-1}^*$ respectively. Now suppose that, on further examination of his own problem, Player 0 discovers that there is some $s_0^{**} \in S_0$ such that

$$M_0(s_0^{**}, s_1^*, \cdots, s_{n-1}) > M_0(s_0^*, \cdots, s_i, \cdots, s_{n-1}) \ ,$$

that is, which is better than the putative "best" strategy s_0^*. If this is the case, we must abandon the assumption that the theory which selected $(s_0^*, \cdots, s_{n-1}^*)$ as "best" for the respective players is a satisfactory one.

This consideration leads us to require that the following condition be satisfied by any solution to a game: If $(s_0^*, \cdots, s_i^*, \cdots, s_{n-1}^*)$ is a *solution* to the game, then

$$M_i(s_0^*, \cdots, s_i^*, \cdots, s_{n-1}^*) \geq M_i(s_0^*, \cdots, s_i, \cdots, s_{n-1}^*) \qquad (5\text{-}2)$$

for all $s_i \in S_i$ and for $i = 0, 1, \cdots, n - 1$. If (5-2) is satisfied by

$$(s_0^*, \cdots, s_i^*, \cdots, s_{n-1}^*) \ ,$$

---

[9] A recent manuscript by John C. Harsanyi, *Rational Behavior and Bargaining Equilibrium in Games and Social Situations*, appears to represent a considerable advance in the theory of cooperative games. It became available to the author just prior to the completion of this monograph.

we will call it an *equilibrium point* of the game. A necessary condition for a point in $\Pi_i S_i$ to be a solution to the game, therefore, is that it be an equilibrium point.[10]

Nash[11] has proven the existence of an equilibrium point for any non-cooperative game in which the sets S'_t of *pure* strategies are finite; this equilibrium point may, however, exist only among the mixed strategies.[12] Uniqueness of the equilibrium point is not guaranteed. Moreover, if $(s_0^*, \cdots, s_i^*, \cdots, s_{n-1}^*)$ and $(s_0^{**}, \cdots, s_i^{**}, \cdots, s_{n-1}^{**})$ are both equilibrium points of a given game, it is not in general true that $(s_0^*, \cdots, s_i^{**}, \cdots, s_{n-1}^*)$ is an equilibrium point, that is, that equilibrium strategies are interchangeable. Nor is it generally true in such a case that

$$M_i(s_0^*, \cdots, s_i^*, \cdots, s_{n-1}^*) = M_i(s_0^{**}, \cdots, s_i^{**}, \cdots, s_{n-1}^{**})$$

for all i, that is, that equilibrium strategies are payoff-equivalent. Hence the equilibrium point theory is not a completely satisfactory solution theory whenever the equilibrium points are not unique.

5.1.4. Application to 2-Person Zero-Sum Games

While the theory of 2-person zero-sum (i.e., strictly competitive) games is not directly relevant to the bidding problem,[13] it is the best-known part of the general theory, and so we will use it here to illustrate the equilibrium point concept.

By definition, in a 2-person zero-sum game,

$$M_1(s_0, s_1) = -M_0(s_0, s_1) , \qquad \text{for all} \qquad s_i \,\epsilon\, S_i, \, i = 0, 1 . \qquad (5\text{-}3)$$

The game will have an equilibrium point at (s_0^*, s_1^*) if and only if both

$$M_0(s_0^*, s_1^*) \geq M_0(s_0, s_1^*) \qquad \text{for all} \qquad s_0 \,\epsilon\, S_0 \qquad (5\text{-}4)$$

and

$$M_1(s_0^*, s_1^*) \geq M_1(s_0^*, s_1) \qquad \text{for all} \qquad s_1 \,\epsilon\, S_1 . \qquad (5\text{-}5)$$

Substituting from (5-3) into (5-5), the latter condition becomes

$$M_0(s_0^*, s_1^*) \leq M_0(s_0^*, s_1) \qquad \text{for all} \qquad s_1 \,\epsilon\, S_1 . \qquad (5\text{-}6)$$

Therefore, combining (5-4) and (5-6), there will be an equilibrium point at (s_0^*, s_1^*) if and only if

$$M_0(s_0, s_1^*) \leq M_0(s_0^*, s_1^*) \leq M_0(s_0^*, s_1) \qquad (5\text{-}7)$$

for all $s_0 \,\epsilon\, S_0$ and $s_1 \,\epsilon\, S_1$, that is, if (s_0^*, s_1^*) is a saddle point of M_0.

Suppose that a 2-person zero-sum game has a saddle point[14] at (s_0^*, s_1^*) and

---

[10] It is not, however, required that every equilibrium point be a solution.

[11] "Equilibrium Points in *n*-Person Games," Proceedings of the National Academy of Sciences, Vol. 36 (1950), pp. 48–49.

[12] If all the information sets in a game contain only a single node (in which case the game is called a "game of perfect information,") the game will have a pure strategy equilibrium point. See McKinsey, *op. cit.*, pp. 130–134.

[13] However, Lawrence Friedman, in a Ph.D. thesis at Case Institute of Technology, did treat bidding as a zero-sum game.

[14] The existence of a saddle point is guaranteed by the Nash equilibrium point theorem, *op. cit.*, n. 10, for all games with finite pure strategy sets; in addition, there are a number of existence theorems tailored especially to the 2-person zero-sum case; see Luce and Raiffa, *op. cit.*, p. 390, for a survey. Existence of a saddle point can also be proven if the two pure strategy sets are the unit continuum and the payoff function M_0 is continuous in the closed unit square; see McKinsey, *op. cit.*, pp. 186–193.

that the quantities

$$\max_{s_0} \min_{s_1} M_0(s_0, s_1) \quad \text{and} \quad \min_{s_1} \max_{s_0} M_0(s_0, s_1)$$

exist[15] for $s_0 \in S_0$ and $s_1 \in S_1$. Then it can be shown[16] that

$$\max_{s_0} \min_{s_1} M_0(s_0, s_1) = M_0(s_0^*, s_1^*) = \min_{s_1} \max_{s_0} M_0(s_0, s_1) . \tag{5-8}$$

Thus, the equilibrium point theory leads to the familiar rule in 2-person zero-sum theory that Player 0 should choose s_0 to maximize $\min_{s_1} M_0(s_0, s_1)$, which has been called his *security level;* and Player 1, correspondingly, should choose s_1 to minimize $\max_{s_0} M_0(s_0, s_1)$. The resulting choices will be in equilibrium. This prescription is generally called the *minimax criterion.* (Note that the equilibrium property of minimax solutions is true in general only for 2-person zero-sum games.)

5.2. The Single-Play Bidding Game

In this section, we will begin our attack on the bidding problem by abstracting it into an *n*-person non-cooperative game which is to be played once and only once. We will demonstrate the existence of an equilibrium point for this game and the uniqueness of the equilibrium payoff.

5.2.1. Characterization of the Game

A game can be characterized, as indicated in Sec. 5.1.1, by specifying: (1) the sets of strategies available to the players; and (2) the payoff functions of the players.

1. *Strategy sets.* Player i, for $i = 0, 1, \cdots, n - 1$, chooses a positive real number b_i from the closed unit interval $[0, 1]$. For the time being we will restrict our attention to pure strategies.

Before introducing the payoff functions, we require a few preliminaries. Let $b^* = \max_i \{b_i\}$, the highest bid. Define

$$W \equiv \{i : b_i = b^*\} ,$$

the set of indices of the winning bidders (tie bids are admitted). Define

$$\delta_i = \begin{cases} 1 & i \in W \\ 0 & i \notin W , \end{cases} \quad \text{if}$$

and define

$$r = \sum_{i=0}^{n-1} \delta_i ,$$

the number of winning bidders.

---

[15] They will exist, in particular, if (1) both sets of pure strategies are finite, or (2) each set of pure strategies is the unit continuum and the payoff function is continuous in the closed unit square.

[16] McKinsey, *op. cit.,* p. 12–13.

2. *Payoff functions.* Player i, for $i = 0, 1, \cdots, n - 1$, receives a payoff of

$$M_i(b_0, \cdots, b_i, \cdots, b_{n-1}) = (\delta_i/r)(1 - b_i) \ . \tag{5-9}$$

The payoff function (5-9) can be justified on the following assumptions, which would not be tolerable if we sought to compute a precise solution to a particular real-world bidding problem but which may suffice to indicate the qualitative nature of such a solution:

1. Each player (bidding group) seeks to maximize the monetary expected value of its strategy.
2. Each player values the outcome of losing the bid at $0; in Chapter 3 we have justified the exclusion of expenses not dependent on the amount of the bid.   For the value of winning the bid, we take the expected net revenue (total proceeds minus inventory costs) as defined in Chapter 4, minus estimated selling and underwriting costs.
3. The players have identical expectations of net revenues and selling costs, so that they are in agreement on the value of winning the bid.   In addition, each of them recognizes that they are in agreement.   This latter assumption meets the game-theoretic requirement that players be informed of their opponents' payoff functions.
4. If there are r bidders tied for high bid, they divide the issue equally among themselves.   It will be recalled that the actual procedure in case of ties in the high bid is generally to have a second bidding in which each of the tied bidders has the opportunity of raising his bid.   Since the high bid in the second bidding cannot be less than the original high bid, assumption (4) may slightly overstate the actual payoff expectation of tied high bidders. This fact will not be of critical importance in the analysis, however.

On the assumption that all players assign the same value to winning the bid, we can, without loss of generality, normalize this value and call it 1.   This normalization, which corresponds simply to changing the unit of measurement of money, leads to the payoff function (5-9).

The bidding problem, even with only two players, must be classified as a non-strictly competitive game, since it is easy to show that there exist sets of strategies over which the interests of the players are not strictly opposing.   Suppose, for example, that in a 2-person game Player 0 employs strategy b_0 while Player 1 employs strategy b_1, where $1 \geq b_1 > b_0$.   Then the payoff to Player 0 is 0 while that to Player 1 is $1 - b_1$.   Now Player 1 can lower his bid and, so long as $b_1 > b_0$, he will gain but not at the expense of Player 1, whose payoff will be unaffected.

Since the 2-person bidding game is non-strictly competitive, it is also non-zero-sum; i.e., the sum of the payoffs accruing to the players from any strategy pair is, in general, not zero.   This situation would be changed if we introduced the issuer as a third player who loses whatever the winning bidder gains.   It is difficult, however, to formalize the issuer's strategic opportunities.   In the ensuing analysis, therefore, we will restrict the issuer's strategy to the acceptance of the high bid, whatever it is.

Any one of Player 0's pure strategies has a security level of 0. That is, the most that Player 0 can assure himself by his choice of b_0 is 0, since Player 1 can always hold Player 0 down to this level by choosing, e.g., $b_1 = 1$.

Formally, $\min\limits_{b_1} M(b_0, b_1) = 0$ for all b_0. Therefore, $\max\limits_{b_0} \min\limits_{b_1} M_0(b_0, b_1) = 0$.
So far as maximizing his security level is concerned, therefore, Player 0 can pick any one of his pure strategies; they are all equally desirable (or undesirable) by the security level criterion.

The corresponding argument for Player 1 indicates that all of his pure strategies likewise "maximize" his security level.

Thus the minimax criterion does not seem to be of much help in picking out a "best" strategy for either player in this game, at least if our attention is restricted to pure strategies. We remember, however, that the minimax principle is justified in 2-person strictly competitive games primarily on the grounds that if and only if both players adopt this criterion, the resultant outcome will be in equilibrium. In non-strictly competitive games, on the other hand, it is not necessarily true that minimax strategies are in equilibrium or that equilibrium strategies are minimax.

5.2.2. Pure Strategy Equilibrium Points

The principal result regarding pure strategy equilibrium points in the single-play bidding game are expressed in the following

Theorem: The n-person single-play bidding game with $n > 1$ has an equilibrium point at $(b_0, b_1, \cdots, b_{n-1})$ if and only if $b^* = 1$ and $r(W) > 1$.

▶ To prove this theorem, we will consider separately the four cases:

(a) $b^* = 1$ and $r(W) > 1$; (b) $b^* = 1$ and $r(W) = 1$;
(c) $b^* < 1$ and $r(W) = 1$; and (d) $b^* < 1$ and $r(W) > 1$.

We will show that equilibrium points exist only for case (a).

Case (a). If $b^* = 1$, then $M_i(b_0, b_1, \cdots, b_{n-1}) = 0$ for all i. Moreover, no player can improve his payoff by unilateral action (for $i \in W$, this conclusion requires that $r(W) > 1$). Therefore, $(b_0, b_1, \cdots, b_{n-1})$ is an equilibrium point.

Case (b). The payoffs are as in case (a). However, since $r(W) = 1$, the single player who is bidding $b^* = 1$ can improve his payoff unilaterally by reducing his bid to $1 - \epsilon$, so long as $1 - \epsilon$ is greater than or equal to the next higher bid. Therefore, $(b_0, b_1, \cdots, b_{n-1})$ cannot be an equilibrium point.

Case (c). If $b^* < 1$ and $r(W) = 1$, then $M_i(b_0, b_1, \cdots, b_{n-1})$ is $(1 - b^*)$ for $i \in W$ and 0 otherwise. Each $i \notin W$ can increase his payoff unilaterally by raising his bid to b^*. Therefore, $(b_0, b_1, \cdots, b_{n-1})$ cannot be an equilibrium point.

Case (d). If $b^* < 1$ and $r(W) > 1$, then $M_i(b_0, b_1, \cdots, b_{n-1})$ is $(1 - b^*)/r$ for $i \in W$. Each $i \in W$ can increase his payoff unilaterally by raising his bid so long as there exists an $\epsilon > 0$ such that

$$\frac{1 - b^*}{r} < 1 - b^* - \epsilon \;,$$

or, equivalently, such that

$$0 < \epsilon < (1 - b^*)/r \;.$$

But such an ϵ exists unless $b^* = 1$. Therefore, $(b_0, b_1, \cdots, b_{n-1})$ cannot be an equilibrium point. Q.E.D.   ◀

At equilibrium, therefore, at least two players must be bidding 1, and the payoff to all players will be 0. It is of interest to note that, contrary to what might have been expected, the equilibrium conditions do not depend on n, the number of players, so long as $n > 1$.

While the equilibrium point concept is very compelling given the assumption of symmetric rationality, the equilibrium strategies in the single-play bidding game have one very distressing feature. They are all dominated, in the sense that Player i can do at least as well with any other strategy as he can with $b_i = 1$, and he may do better with some other strategy if the other players also fail to bid 1. We will return to this consideration later.

5.3. The Repeated-Play Bidding Game

In the preceding section we treated the bidding game as if it were to be played once and only once. Its real-world counterpart is not played only once, however, and it is therefore of interest to determine the strategic differences which arise when play is to be repeated.

An obvious difference is the frightful increase in the complexity of the problem. Each player must now be concerned with the effect of his choice at each stage of the play on the subsequent choices of his opponents. On the other hand, he must also decide what influence his opponents' past choices should have on his choice at a given stage. In short, the concept of strategy discussed earlier in this chapter appears with full force in the repeated bidding game.

Offsetting the greater analytical complexity of the repeated game, it offers the possibility of greater average payoffs to the players than they could attain by equilibrium choices in the single-play game. We will formalize this notion shortly, but first we will give an informal argument designed to render the conclusion plausible.

In the singly-played game, it was postulated that the players could not communicate prior to the bidding in order to coordinate their strategies. We will continue to maintain this assumption. If the game is to be repeated, however, there is an opportunity for the players to "communicate" in a way which the rules cannot prevent—through their previous actions.

In a 2-person game, for example, Player 0 might bid $b_0 < 1$ on a number of successive trials, which would not be in equilibrium in a single-play game, hoping by this action to encourage Player 1 to accept b_0 as a reasonable bid at which each player can make a "fair" return. Player 1, in considering whether or not to follow Player 0's lead, must consider the probability that, if he attempts to cut Player 0 out of the bidding by entering bids greater than b_0, Player 0 will eventually be forced to come up to this higher level. At the higher level, neither player will make as much as he would make had Player 0's lead been followed. Hence it is reasonable to expect that under some conditions a pattern of bidding will develop which would not be in equilibrium if only single plays were considered.

The pattern thus established may even be in "equilibrium" in the repeated-play game, in the sense that neither player will be much inclined to deviate from the established pattern so long as he expects his opponent to stick with it, since he knows that his opponent is capable of retaliating on the bid following the deviation. Considering the long run, therefore, each player's interests may be best served by adhering to the established pattern of behavior, so that this pattern will be in "equilibrium." The equilibrating process which takes place in repeated-play games has suggestively been called "temporal collusion" and is characteristic of "price leadership."

It must be observed that this equilibrium can be a very unstable one. It is based on the expectation by each player that his opponent will continue to conform. If anything happens to upset this expectation, it seems likely that both players will start tending toward one of the single-play equilibria. For example, suppose that after a number of repetitions in which each player has bid b_0, Player 0 deviates to $b_0 + \epsilon$ and wins. On the next play, it will appear to Player 1 that he has no choice but to bid at least $b_0 + \epsilon$. This process may continue until a single-play equilibrium has been reached.

This situation may be recognized as typical of a price war. So long as every seller in a particular market adheres to what has become the established price, all is serene. But let one lower his price in an effort to increase his share of the market and the others are forced to follow to hold their clientele. Eventually a new equilibrium may be reached at a lower price, or one seller may take the lead in attempting to return to the old level. Very possibly none of the sellers, not even the maverick, will benefit by the price war, and anticipation of this fact will tend to discourage price cutting.

5.3.1. *Formal Characterization*

The preceding discussion, with its picture of players constantly adjusting their bids in response to the history of their opponents' bids, illustrates the complexity of the strategic problem in repeated play. In order to cope with this complexity, we will make some fairly drastic simplifying assumptions in the course of our formal analysis. Despite these simplifications, we feel that the model we will use is sufficiently close to reality to give a good qualitative indication of the effects of repeated play on the strategic problem.

The model we will use is that of a *game of economic survival*. The theory was developed originally by M. Shubik and G. L. Thompson[17] as a non-strictly competitive extension of the strictly-competitive theory of games of survival.[18] The theory forms an important foundation of Shubik's recent book on the application of the game theory to the problem of describing the structure of economic markets.[19]

The game of economic survival we will use as a model for the repeated bidding problem may be specified as follows:

1. The game consists of a (denumerably) infinite number of trials, equally spaced in time at $t = 0, 1, 2, \cdots$. In practice, of course, an infinity of issues is unlikely ever to exist, although the actual number may be quite large and is in any event unknown. Since we do not know enough about the real world to describe it with complete accuracy, we take the easy way out and use an approximation which is simple to work with mathematically.

2. Each trial is identical with the single-play game previously discussed. Hidden in this assumption are the following sub-assumptions: (a) The value of winning the bid is the same in each trial and as usual is normalized as 1; (b) on each trial, each player selects a bid b_i from the closed interval $[0, 1]$; and (c) the number n and the identity of the players is the same on each trial. No attempt is made to justify these assumptions on realistic grounds, since we are interested only in the qualitative nature of the conclusions.

3. We will assume that each player values a payoff to be received t trials hence at ρ^t times the value of the same payoff received immediately, where $0 < \rho < 1$. (ρ is a discount, or present value, factor.) If r is the rate of return which each player wishes to earn in the interval between trials (*not* per annum), then $\rho = 1/(1 + r)$. It is not, of course, realistic to expect that a given player will have the same discount rate over all future intervals, much less that all players will agree on this rate, but once again the approximation does not seem too gross and it will be convenient to work with.

5.3.2. Stationary Strategy Equilibrium Points

Instead of considering the tremendous variety of strategies which are possible, we will in the main restrict ourselves to a class of strategies called *stationary strategies* by Shubik.[20] In the bidding game, a stationary strategy consists of naming the same bid on each trial. It seems reasonable to consider the class of stationary strategies since, in view of the assumptions made in the last section, each player is faced with precisely the same decision problem on each trial.

If all of the players employ stationary strategies, the set of winning bidders will be identical on each trial and the payoffs on each trial will be as given by (5-9). Each player will, therefore, receive a discounted payoff for the entire game which is

$$\sum_{t=0}^{\infty} \rho^t = 1/(1 - \rho)$$

[17] "Games of Economic Survival," *Naval Research Logistics Quarterly*, June 1959.
[18] See Luce and Raiffa, *op. cit.*, p. 467 ff.
[19] M. Shubik, *Strategy and Market Structure*.
[20] *Ibid.*, p. 228.

times the payoff he would receive with the corresponding bid in the single-play game.

Since the stationary strategy payoffs are proportional to the single-play payoffs, so long as each player is restricted to his stationary strategies it is clear that he should choose exactly as he would in a single-play game. Therefore, the results of Sec. 5.2.2 may be extended to this case if we now interpret b_i as a stationary strategy of Player i. We restate the result here in its modified form:

Theorem. Let b_i be the stationary strategy in which Player i bids b_i on each trial of a repeated-play game, and let each player be restricted to choosing such a stationary strategy. Then $(b_0, b_1, \cdots, b_{n-1})$ will be an equilibrium point if and only if $b^* = 1$ and $r(W) > 1$ on each trial.

5.3.3. *Response Strategies*

It is the possibility of retaliation that may make repeated play games different from single play games. We will consider two types of retaliatory action which might be taken against a player who deviates from a previously established bidding pattern:

1. In the *weak response,* each of the opponents responds to a deviation by bidding the same as the deviant on each repetition following the deviation.
2. In the *strong response,* at least one of the opponents responds to a deviation by immediately bidding 1 on the issue following the deviation and continuing to bid 1 on each issue thereafter.

We will consider whether the anticipation of either of these types of response can be effective in maintaining a stationary strategy equilibrium point with $b^* < 1$; one that would *not* be in equilibrium on a single play.

First we note that if such a point exists, all the players must be submitting identical bids on each trial, so that the discounted payoff to each player from such a bid b can be represented by

$$V(b) = (1 - b)/n + \rho V(b)$$

or

$$V(b) = (1 - b)/n(1 - \rho) \ . \tag{5-10}$$

▶ The assertion that if there is an equilibrium point with $b^* < 1$, then $r(W) = n$ on each trial follows from the application of case (c) of Sec. 5.2.2 to stationary strategies. ◀

Weak response. If, on a given trial, all players hold at b except one who deviates by some $\epsilon > 0$, and then all players match this deviation on all subsequent trials, the payoff to the deviant player will be $(1 - b - \epsilon)$ on the trial on which he deviates and $V(b + \epsilon)$ on all subsequent trials. A deviation will be profitable, therefore, if there exists an $\epsilon > 0$ such that

$$(1 - b - \epsilon) + \rho V(b + \epsilon) > V(b) \ . \tag{5-11}$$

By substitution from (5-10), this last condition becomes

$$(1 - b - \epsilon)[1 + \rho/n(1 - \rho] > (1 - b)/n(1 - \rho) \; ,$$

or, upon simplification and rearrangement of terms,

$$\epsilon < (1 - b) \frac{(n - 1)(1 - \rho)}{n(1 - \rho) + \rho} \; . \tag{5-12}$$

But an ϵ satisfying (5-12) always exists unless $b = 1$. Therefore we have proven that the weak response threat is not sufficient to make any stationary strategy point an equilibrium point which would not be in equilibrium if the players were restricted to their stationary strategies.

Strong response. If, on a given trial, all players hold at b except one who deviates by some $\epsilon > 0$, and then *at least one* opponent bids 1 on all subsequent trials, the payoff to the deviant player will be $(1 - b - \epsilon)$ on the trial on which he deviates and 0 on all subsequent trials. A deviation will be profitable, therefore, if there exists an $\epsilon > 0$ such that

$$(1 - b - \epsilon) > (1 - b)/n(1 - \rho) \; ,$$

which, upon simplification and rearrangement of terms, becomes

$$\epsilon < (1 - b) \left[\frac{n(1 - \rho) - 1}{n(1 - \rho)} \right] \; . \tag{5-13}$$

An ϵ satisfying (5-13) exists unless: (a) $b = 1$; or (b) $b < 1$ but $\rho > 1 - 1/n$. In the latter cases, the bracketed term becomes negative and hence requires ϵ to be negative, contrary to the requirement that $\epsilon > 0$.

Against the threat of a strong response, therefore, *any* stationary strategy can be in equilibrium provided that ρ is sufficiently high, i.e., provided that the players value future payoffs highly enough;[21] otherwise the results are equivalent to the single-play equilibrium.

5.3.4. *The Credibility Problem*

It is of interest to see what can be said about the relative desirability of the two response strategies we have analyzed. If some rationale could be developed for asserting that one of these responses is better than the other, then we might argue that each player would be well advised to assume that his opponents were committed to that "better" response and to act accordingly.

The strong response, of course, has the advantage that, even with relatively high discounting of future payoffs, it makes available to the players more favorable equilibrium payoffs than they could achieve with the weak response. At first glance this might seem to be a compelling case for identifying the strong response as the "better" one.

The trouble with the strong response is suggested by the following example. Suppose, in a two-player repeated game Player 0 is attempting to enforce a bidding level of b by the threat of a strong response, where $b < 1$ and hence is not in

---

[21] If there are only two players, any stationary strategy can be in equilibrium unless $\rho < 1 - \frac{1}{2} = .5$. This implies that each player must expect to earn more than 100% on capital in the interval between trials.

equilibrium against the weak response. Player 1 may then reason as follows: "Suppose I deviate to $b + \epsilon$. Will Player 1 respond to such a deviation by bidding 1 on all subsequent plays? If he does, his payoff (as well as mine) will be 0 on all of these plays. Suppose, on the other hand, he adopts the weak response. In that case we each receive a payoff of $(1 - b - \epsilon)/2$. In other words, *given that I have already deviated*, Player 0's best response (of the two) is the weak response. Hence it seems to me that Player 0 is much more likely to adopt the weak response than the strong response, and therefore it would pay me to deviate."

The trouble with the strong response, as the example shows, is that it lacks *credibility*.

Of course, the players can improve the credibility of a strong threat if they have the opportunity of committing themselves. For example, if a bidder could enter into a side contract which subjected him to a heavy penalty if he failed to follow through on a strong threat, then his economic interest might well cause him to follow through.

An analogy, though not a complete one, is to be found in U.S.-Soviet relations in the post-World War II period.[22] The United States has been following a policy of containment of the Soviet Union; we may say that it has been attempting to enforce the present division of the world into Eastern and Western blocs as a stationary strategy equilibrium point. To enforce this equilibrium the United States has had the choice of essentially two responses to any Soviet deviation from the status quo: massive retaliation (the strong response) and limited warfare (the weak response).

During the period of U.S. nuclear monopoly, the strong response had a high degree of credibility, since U.S. losses from all-out strategic bombardment were likely to be much less than those of the Soviet Union. At the present time, however, most experts feel that the balance of power is such that the losses to the two sides in a nuclear war would be of roughly the same order of magnitude. This situation robs the massive retaliation strategy of much of its credibility, by exactly the same type of argument as we used in the bidding game.

Continuing the analogy, to some extent the credibility of the massive retaliation strategy can be increased by public commitments made by the United States. For example, the loss of prestige and world position we would suffer by failing to come to the aid of an ally whom we have publicly promised to defend is a penalty which must make our massive retaliation threat more plausible to the Soviet Union. (Needless to say, the Soviet leadership has also been aware of the advantage of commitments.)

Returning to the bidding game, we conclude that the strong response has high effectiveness conditional on its credibility but its credibility is low; while the weak response has relatively low effectiveness but high credibility. These contrasting considerations must be balanced off in order to determine the better response.

In a game in which each player has a reputation for thorough-going rationality, the credibility of the strong response must be rated as virtually nil (unless commitments have been made), since the reasoning attributed to Player 1 earlier in this

[22] For similar discussion, see Schelling, *The Strategy of Conflict*, pp. 53–81.

section is then controlling. If, on the other hand, the players are *not* convinced of the complete rationality of their opponents, they must allow for the chance that some "damn fool" will follow through on a strong response threat. The conclusion to be drawn from this is that it may be of advantage to a player to have the reputation of being a "damn fool"; this will increase the credibility of his strong threats and hence his (and everyone else's) equilibrium payoffs.

We believe that most investment bankers are reasonable rational men not given to cutting their own figurative throats if they can avoid it. So much the worse for them; we believe that, as a result, the balance between credibility and effectiveness probably falls on the side of the weak response. At the same time, as long as any element of doubt about the rationality of opponents remains, the potentiality of a strong response may exert some influence on a bidder's decision whether or not to deviate from an established bidding pattern.

Another way of looking at this decision leads to the same conclusion although from slightly different premises. We have heretofore restricted ourselves to consideration of only two relatively extreme responses to a deviation. In practice intermediate cases are feasible. A player may adopt the following response: after a deviation, bid 1 for the next t bids, then return to the old bidding level. This response punishes the deviant more than the weak response but less than the strong response; it is therefore of intermediate conditional effectiveness. At the same time, it is less costly to the punisher than the strong response and hence perhaps more credible. On balance, therefore, a response of this sort may be preferable to either the strong or the weak response. At the same time we conjecture that its overall effectiveness, adjusted for credibility, will not be too different from that of the weak response.

Finally, it should be observed that it requires the tacit consent of *all* bidders to establish a stationary strategy equilibrium point. If there is only one bidder who will not accept a given point, it cannot be maintained. For this reason, it is possible that the number of players has a more critical role than an analytical model has indicated, in that it will be more difficult to assure the cooperation of all players when the number is large.

Our tentative conclusion, therefore, is that the actual behavior of investment banking groups in competitive bidding will be close to that predicted by the weak response model. We will examine some evidence on this point later in the chapter.

5.4. Relevance of the Game-Theoretic Analysis

Throughout most of the earlier sections of this chapter we have been discussing an abstract game. This abstract game has analogies with the real-world bidding problem, and from time to time we have called attention to these analogies. We would now like to pull these references together into a coherent statement of the relevance of the abstract game to the real-world bidding problem.

There are two ways, not necessarily mutually exclusive, in which game theory can be interpreted. The first is as a *descriptive* theory which predicts how persons will actually behave when confronted with a game-type situation. The other is as a *normative* theory, which prescribes how a person ought to behave in order to achieve certain objectives.

Descriptive theory is, of course, also useful in a normative sense. It is normatively valuable to one bidder to be able to predict the behavior of his competitors; this requires a descriptive theory of this behavior. If, for example, all bidders except one were committed to the employment of an equilibrium strategy (a descriptive statement), then that one bidder would be well advised to employ the same strategy (a normative statement). Conversely, as we have already argued at several points, the normative relevance to any player of the equilibrium concept is weakened if it appears that it is not descriptively valid when applied to his competitors.

5.4.1. *Descriptive Relevance of Game Analysis*

Strictly speaking, game theory by itself does not predict behavior; it merely defines the conditions under which certain behavioral patterns will be in equilibrium. We can arrive at a descriptive theory, however, by appending to game theory the assertion that real-world decision makers faced with game-type problems will adopt equilibrium patterns of behavior.

Several of the conditions postulated by game theory—notably, knowledge of opponents' payoff functions—are obviously not realized in the real-world bidding problem.[23] Hence the most that can be said for game theory is that it is approximate; i.e., that bidders "tend" to adopt equilibrium strategies. We have already discussed some directions in which the strict game-theoretic results must be modified to reflect these differences in conditions.

With these qualifications, let us turn to the question of determining the sort of behavior that is predicted by the equilibrium theory. The principal prediction is that a bidder will submit a bid which is quite close to the value he assigns to winning the issue—perhaps a bit lower because of uncertainty regarding payoffs, uncertainty regarding the opponents' rationality, and temporal collusion.

In Sec. 5.2.1 we defined the value of winning the bid as the expected net revenue less estimated selling and underwriting costs. Let us assume that the model of Sec. 4.1 is valid and that, therefore, the optimum price p^* (as a fraction of par value) is given by

$$p^* = p_c + \frac{1}{k\alpha} \, , \tag{4-16'}$$

where p_c is the price which would insure immediate sale of the bonds, k is the inventory carrying charge, and α is the market reaction parameter defined implicitly by (4-13). If p^* is adopted as the public offering price, we have shown in Sec. 4.1.3 that expected net revenue is given by

$$\mathrm{E}[R(p^*)] = q \left(\bar{p}_c + \frac{1}{2k\alpha} - \frac{k\alpha \breve{p}_c}{2} \right) \, , \tag{4-21}$$

[23] In Chapter 6 we will consider the effect of uncertainty regarding one's opponents' payoffs and will show that this uncertainty will generally lead to somewhat lower bids than the game-theoretic equilibria.

where q is the par value of the issue, $\overline{p}_c$ is the mean, and $\breve{p}_c$ is the variance of the distribution of $\tilde{p}_c$. Let

$\hat{b} =$ predicted bid as a fraction of par value;

$m =$ selling and underwriting costs as a fraction of par value.

We can then formalize the predicted behavior of bidders as follows:

$$\hat{b} = \overline{p}_c + \frac{1}{2k\alpha} - \frac{k\alpha \breve{p}_c}{2} - m \ . \tag{5-14}$$

It will be more convenient, however, to work with the predicted *spread* defined by

$$\hat{s} \equiv p^* - \hat{b} \ ,$$

since this will enable us to eliminate one variable, $\overline{p}_c$. Combining (4-16') and (5-14), we obtain

$$\hat{s} = \left(\overline{p}_c + \frac{1}{k\alpha}\right) - \left(\overline{p}_c + \frac{1}{2k\alpha} - \frac{k\alpha \breve{p}_c}{2} - m\right)$$

$$= \frac{1}{2k\alpha} + \frac{k\alpha \breve{p}_c}{2} + m \ . \tag{5-15}$$

The three components of the predicted spread can be interpreted as follows. The last component, m, of course, represents the usual accounting costs associated with the operation—selling concessions, management fees, and other underwriting expenses. The first term, $\frac{1}{2}k\alpha$, represents what the cost of carrying inventory would be if the "ideal" price $\tilde{p}_c$ were equal to its expected value $\overline{p}_c$. The center term represents the increase in expected cost of carrying inventory as a result of uncertainty concerning $\tilde{p}_c$, as measured by its variance $\breve{p}_c$. The total predicted spread is then the sum of these three components (or perhaps slightly greater).

We can make at least rough order-of-magnitude estimates of some of the parameters of (5-15). In Sec. 4.1.4 we indicated our opinion that a reasonable estimate of the product $k\alpha$ would be about 100; we also showed, however, that a value of 1,000 is more consistent with observed behavior of bankers. As a compromise, let us use an estimate of 500 in the present analysis.

For an estimate of m, we can use data collected for *U.S.* v. *Morgan et al.* and summarized by Cohan.[24] For several years prior to 1949 (the last year represented by the data), the sum of management fees, selling concessions, and underwriting expenses for Aa-rated public utility bonds was close to .003 of the public offering price. Since price is usually close to par value, we will use this figure of .003 as our estimate of m.

Substituting these estimates of $k\alpha$ and m into (5-15), we arrive at the following expression for predicted spread as a function of $\breve{p}_c$:

$$s = 250\breve{p}_c + .004 \ . \tag{5-16}$$

Table 5.1 gives the predicted spread corresponding to several possible values of the *standard deviation*. Since bidders customarily think in terms of offering

[24] A. B. Cohan, *Cost of Flotation of Long-Term Corporate Debt Since 1935.*

yield rather than offering price, we have given the standard deviation of both variables in the table. (For this purpose, we have assumed a bond issue with a 4% coupon and a 30-year maturity with a public offering price close to par.)

Table 5.1

Relationship of Standard Deviation to Predicted Spread

Standard Deviation		
Yield	Price	Predicted Spread
.00≡	.0000	.00400
.01	.00174	.00476
.02	.00348	.00703
.03	.00523	.01084
.04	.00699	.01621
.05	.00874	.02310
.10	.01759	.08135
.15	.02656	.18036

For example: Assume that the bidding group is willing to assign a Normal subjective distribution to the market clearing yield and that it assigns probability .95 to the statement that the "true" market-clearing yield is within .04% (i.e., four basis points) of expected yield; this implies that the standard deviation of yield is approximately .02%. Note that, within the range of variables under consideration, price is very nearly a linear function of yield. Hence the market-clearing price will also have a Normal subjective distribution and its standard deviation will be .00348 (i.e., $3.48 per $1,000 bond). Substituting this value into (5-16), we determine that the predicted spread is .00703 (i.e., $7.03 per $1,000 bond).

Against the data in the table, we can compare data on actual spreads on competitively bid issues. In 1949, according to the data cited by Cohan,[25] spreads on Aa-rated public utility issues sold by competitive bidding averaged .005. In 1949 the Federal Reserve System was stabilizing the market for U.S. Treasury bonds, with the result that interest rates were quite stable. This fact most likely meant that there was very little uncertainty regarding the market-clearing price for new corporate issues.

In 1957, on the other hand, the bond market was free of government pegging and consequently more uncertainty would attach to the pricing of new corporate issues. For this year, we have calculated that the weighted average spread of equivalently-rated issues[26] was .008. (We do not have information on selling and underwriting costs for 1957).

[25] *Ibid.*

[26] The issues included in this average were all public utility issues of $2 million par value and over graded A1 by Standard and Poor's and offered at competitive bidding in calendar 1957. There were 39 such issues aggregating $976 million in par value. The original data were obtained from *Competitive Sales and Negotiated Public Offerings of New Public Utility. Railroad and Industrial Debt Issues,* compiled by Halsey, Stuart & Co. Inc. Par value was used as the weight.

On the same issues whose average spread in 1957 was calculated to be .008, the weighted average *range* of bids (difference between high and low bids) was also .008. A substantial part of this range is probably a result of differences in price views between bidding groups, and so we can interpret it as a rough measure of uncertainty about price. If we assume that the range estimates six standard deviations (i.e., three standard deviations on either side of the mean), this indicates a standard deviation of about .00133 and therefore a predicted spread of about .00442.

In the foregoing calculations, however, we have used an estimate of α (i.e., 10,000) which is only about half the value of α which is implied by actual pricing behavior of bidders, as calculated in Sec. 4.1.4. What would be the effect on predicted spread of increasing α? Referring to (5-15), we see that α appears in the numerator of one term and the denominator of another. Consequently, for a standard deviation on the order of about .001, the predicted spread is quite insensitive to α. In fact, had we used an estimate of 20,000 for α in the calculations of the last paragraph (rather than 10,000), the predicted spread for 1957 would have been .00438 rather than .00442.

We see that, while actual spreads are quite small relative to par value, they are still larger than predicted by the single-play equilibrium theory (in conjunction with the demand model of Sec. 4.1.3). We would expect actual spreads to be larger to some extent because of the repeated-play phenomena discussed in Sec. 5.3 and because of uncertainty regarding competitors' payoffs. Since we have no exact quantitative prediction of the effects of the factors just mentioned, we cannot conclude that the game-theoretic predictions have been "confirmed" by the data; at the same time, the data are not seriously inconsistent with what we would expect on game-theoretic grounds.

5.4.2. *Normative Relevance of the Game Analysis*

Should investment bankers adhere to equilibrium strategies in competitive bidding? This is a question which must be approached at two levels. First, are equilibrium strategies desirable in the abstract, without regard to how other bidders behave? Second, given that the equilibrium theory is at least approximately valid as a description of his competitor's behavior, as we believe the preceding section suggests, would a given bidder be well advised to employ only equilibrium strategies?

The answer to the first question is, we believe, no. We have indicated reasons for this view in earlier sections of the chapter. Equilibrium strategies are essentially low-profit strategies; there are many non-equilibrium strategies which would be more profitable to the bidders provided that all bidders could settle on them. Unfortunately, in the absence of any possibility for collusion, it appears impossible to formalize a procedure which would make these non-equilibrium points available to the bidders. (This does not necessarily rule out informal processes, such as might be called "custom.")

This point carries us to the second question. Without collusion, there are strong pressures on the bidders to choose equilibrium strategies, and these pressures are mutually reinforcing. That is, if one bidder is committed to an equilibrium strategy, then his competitors have little choice but to follow suit; the answer to the second question, therefore, is yes.

Of course, the pressure toward equilibrium, while undesirable from the position of the investment bankers, works to the advantage of the two other parties at interest in a bond issue; the issuer and the investing public. An increase in profit to the bankers would have to come from one of these two sources. The protection of one or the other of these two parties is the purpose of regulations imposing competitive bidding, and we may conclude that this purpose is well served.

CHAPTER 6

The Bidding Decision: Bayes Analysis

In the preceding chapter we analyzed the competitive bidding problem as a non-cooperative game. While we were able to conclude that the equilibrium concept of such games is at least approximately valid as a *descriptive* theory of actual bidding behavior of investment bankers, from a *normative* point of view the theory has certain flaws:

1. The equilibrium points in the game are all of minimal profitability. Hence, there is little incentive for a bidder to select an equilibrium strategy even though he has no guarantee of doing better with a non-equilibrium strategy. There seems to be a crying need for a method of determining "good" non-equilibrium strategies.
2. Since certain of the assumptions underlying the equilibrium theory—notably perfect knowledge of competitors' payoffs—are not satisfied by the real bidding situation, even the descriptive relevance of the theory is not absolute. A bidder attempting to predict the behavior of his competitors could use a more powerful predictive scheme.

In this chapter we will seek to deal with these two deficiencies through a different line of attack on the bidding problem. Instead of viewing the bidding problem as a symmetric game-type situation in which *each* participant expressly considers his apponents' motivations as a part of his own analysis of the problem, we will treat the problem as a one-person decision problem under uncertainty. Each possible set of opposing bids will be treated as a "state of the world" to which a probability is assigned. Then, on the assumption that a bidding group seeks to maximize expected monetary profit, a bid can be chosen to achieve this objective.

This approach to the bidding problem appears to have been first formulated by the Operations Research Group of Case Institute of Technology and is developed in the doctoral dissertation of Lawrence Friedman.[1] Their results are extended in this chapter, particularly with respect to estimation of the relevant probabilities through the use of Bayesian statistical theory.

---

[1] Friedman, *Competitive Bidding Strategies;* see also Churchman, Ackoff, and Arnoff, *Introduction to Operations Research*, pp. 565–573.

6.1. Determination of the Optimum Bid

6.1.1. Payoff Function

In contrast to the game-theoretic analysis, where we attempted to look simultaneously at the decision problem of all the bidding groups, in the present context we will adopt the point of view of a single group only, which we will call the *bidder*. All other groups bidding on the same issue will be called its *competitors*.

We will assume that the bidder has already determined the value to him (net of all costs except the bid) of winning the bid, and we can without loss of generality, as in the game-theoretic model, normalize the problem by calling this value 1. Exactly the same considerations apply to the determination of this value in the statistical model as in the game model.

A decision by the bidder consists of the choice of a particular positive real number b_0. The return (net of the bid) to the bidder if his bid is high is, therefore, $(1 - b_0)$.

Since the bid of the ith competitor will, in general, be unknown to the bidder, we will consider it to be a random variable $\tilde{b}_i$ whose values are also positive real numbers. We will assume that the bidder is able to assign to the set of opposing bids $(\tilde{b}_1, \cdots, \tilde{b}_n)$ a joint cumulative distribution function $F(\cdot, \cdots, \cdot)$ defined by

$$F(b_1, \cdots, b_n) = Pr\{\tilde{b}_1 \leq b_1, \cdots, \tilde{b}_n \leq b_n\} \ . \tag{6-1}$$

In particular, $F(b_0, \cdots, b_0)$ is the probability that the bidder wins the issue, since it is, by (5-1), the probability that each of his competitors' bids is lower than his. If we define

$$Q(b_0) \equiv F(b_0, \cdots, b_0) \ , \tag{6-2}$$

then the expected monetary value to the bidder resulting from a bid of b_0 can be written as

$$M(b_0) = (1 - b_0)Q(b_0) \ . \tag{6-3}$$

We will assume that the objective of the bidder is to maximize (6-3).

Remark 1. Since the award of an issue is based on cost of money to the issuer rather than on bid price, $F(b_0, \cdots, b_0)$ is the bidder's probability of winning only if all competitors stipulate the same coupon as the bidder. If this is not the case, however, all bids stipulating different coupons can be translated into bids at the bidder's coupon with the same cost of money through use of the definitional relation (3-1b).

Remark 2. We can interpret $Q(b_0)$ as the cumulative probability function of the maximum opposing bid and its derivative, if it exists, as the density function of the maximum opposing bid.

The two factors on the right-hand side of (6-3) may be graphed as in Fig. 6.1, assuming that $Q(\cdot)$ is continuous. Since $(1 - b_0)$ is strictly decreasing in b_0, if only the conditional profit from winning were relevant it would be desirable to make b_0 as low as possible. But $Q(b_0)$ is non-decreasing in b_0, so that probability

73

Figure 6.1

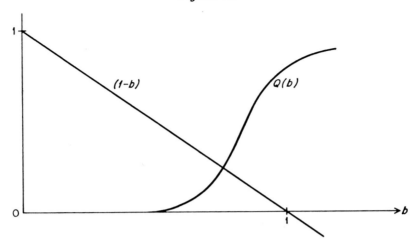

of winning argues for making b_0 as large as possible. These counteracting influences combine to produce a graph of $M(b_0)$ similar to one of those shown in Fig. 6.2.

The exact shape of the graph of $M(b_0)$ will depend upon the form of $Q(b_0)$, and several possibilities are depicted in Fig. 6.2.

Figure 6.2

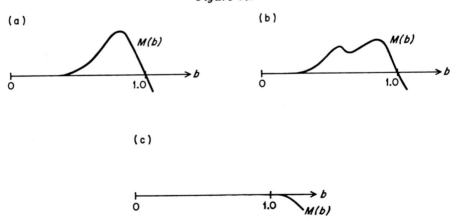

6.1.2. *Optimality Conditions*

Assuming that $Q(\cdot)$ is differentiable, the first-order condition for a maximum of $M(b_0)$ may be obtained by differentiating (6-3), resulting in

$$M'(b_0) = (1 - b_0)q(b_0) - Q(b_0) = 0 , \qquad (6\text{-}4)$$

where $q(b_0) \equiv Q'(b_0)$.

If the bidder is faced with only a single competitor, then $q(\cdot)$ is simply the density function of that competitor's bid. If, on the other hand, there are n competitors, then $q(b_0)$, the density of the maximum competitive bid, must be obtained by differentiating $F(b_1, \cdots, b_n)$ with respect to $b_1, \cdots, b_n$, subject to the condition $b_i = b_0$ for $i = 1, \cdots, n$. This gives

$$q(b_0) = \frac{dF}{db_0} = \sum_{i=1}^{n} \frac{\partial F}{\partial b_i} \cdot \frac{db_i}{db_0} = \sum_{i=1}^{n} \frac{\partial F}{\partial b_i}\bigg|_{b_i = b_0} , \qquad (6\text{-}5)$$

since the side conditions imply $db_i/db_0 = 1$ for $i = 1, \cdots, n$.

In the sequel, it will generally be most convenient to work with the optimality condition in the form

$$q(b_0)/Q(b_0) = 1/(1 - b_0) , \qquad (6\text{-}4')$$

or, if we define $\phi_1(b_0) = q(b_0)/Q(b_0)$ and $\phi_2(b_0) = 1/(1 - b_0)$,

$$\phi_1(b_0) = \phi_2(b_0) . \qquad (6\text{-}4'')$$

Since $\phi_2(b_0)$ is a monotone increasing function in the interval $[0, 1]$, if $\phi_1(b_0)$ is a monotone decreasing function in the same interval, there will be at most one solution of (6-4) in that interval. The function $\phi_1(\cdot)$ has been charted by Schlaifer[2] for the case where $Q(\cdot)$ is the standardized Normal cumulative function; values for the general Normal distribution may be obtained from the same chart through the usual transformation of variables. In the case of the Normal distribution, $\phi_1(\cdot)$ is monotone decreasing.

6.1.3. Computational Considerations

Since (6-4) does not give the optimum bid in closed form, it is necessary to resort to numerical methods of solution.

For the numerical examples later in this chapter, an iterative method of solution of (6-4'') was used which appears to be a good procedure for practical computations. Starting at an initial guess $b^{(0)}$ at the solution b^*, successive approximations to the solution were calculated by the recursion

$$b^{(t+1)} = \phi_2^{-1}[\phi_1(b^{(t)})] . \qquad (6\text{-}6)$$

The successive approximations will converge if, for $|b^* - b| < |b^* - b^{(0)}|$, the ratio $\phi_1'(b)/\phi_2'(b)$ is less than 1 in absolute value.[3] This will usually be assured in practice because of a combination of several considerations. First, we would normally expect the optimum bid to be quite close to 1, for reasons given in the preceding chapter, so that in the neighborhood of the optimum $\phi_2'(b)$ will be positive and quite large. Second, $\phi_1'(b)$ must in any case be less than $\phi_2'(b)$ in the neighborhood of b^* by virtue of the second-order condition for a maximum. Therefore we need only be concerned with the possibility that $-\phi_1'(b) > \phi_2'(b)$; this possibility can normally be dismissed if $Q(\cdot)$ is well-behaved and assigns positive probability

---

[2] *Probability and Statistics for Business Decisions*, Chart IV. Irving LaValle has prepared similar charts for other distributions.

[3] Cf. Courant, *Differential and Integral Calculus*, Vol. I, p. 358. If the approximations do not converge for the recursion (6-6), they will if the inverse of that function is used; if the distributions are given only in tabular form, however, it is less convenient to calculate ϕ_1^{-1} than ϕ_2^{-1}.

to competitive bids greater than 1, which seems likely in view of uncertainty about the value the competitor assigns to the issue.

If the initial trial value is well-chosen, we might expect that, for

$$|b^* - b| < |b^* - b^{(0)}| ,$$

the functions $\phi_1(\cdot)$ and $\phi_2(\cdot)$ can be approximated by their linear parts. In such a case, therefore, we can[4] approximate the recursion formula (6-6) by the linear difference equation

$$b^{(t+1)} \doteq Ab^{(t)} + B . \qquad (6\text{-}6')$$

To determine the coefficients A and B, we first perform two iterations of (6-6), giving the trial values $b^{(0)}$, $b^{(1)}$, and $b^{(2)}$. Substituting these values into (6-6'), we have two equations in the two unknown coefficients. Solving these equations gives us

$$A = (b^{(2)} - b^{(1)})/(b^{(1)} - b^{(0)}) , \quad \text{and}$$
$$B = [(b^{(1)})^2 - b^{(0)}b^{(2)}]/(b^{(1)} - b^{(0)}) .$$

For $|A| < 1$, which is guaranteed by the convergence of (6-6), the sequence generated by (6-6') approaches the limit[5]

$$b^{**} = B/(1 - A)$$
$$= [(b^{(1)})^2 - b^{(0)}b^{(2)}]/(b^{(0)} - 2b^{(1)} + b^{(2)}) . \qquad (6\text{-}7)$$

After calculating $b^{(0)}$, $b^{(1)}$, and $b^{(2)}$, therefore, we could use b^{**} as our next trial value of b^*. This value can then be tested by substitution into (6-6) to see whether it provides the desired degree of accuracy; if not, further iterations may be performed.

6.1.4.   *Problems in Assessment of Multivariate Distributions*

A number of practical problems must be resolved in assessing the joint probability distribution of competitors' bids, among them being the following:[6]

1. Joint distributions are, in general, inherently harder to assess than marginal distributions because of the necessity to reflect the independence of the variables. The exception is when the variables are mutually independent, in which case the joint distribution can be assessed through the marginals on the individual variables. It does not seem reasonable to assume, however, that competitors' bids are mutually independent.[7]

2. The number of active competitors will vary from one issue to another. Suppose that there are a total of N potential competitors in the industry

[4] See Goldberg, *Introduction to Difference Equations*, pp. 180–181.

[5] *Ibid.*

[6] It is not usually practical to keep the formation of a competitive bidding group secret, and so an investment banking group is not generally faced with the situation, considered by Friedman, *op. cit.*, of facing an unknown number of competitors.

[7] But see Churchman, et al., *op. cit.*, in which it is implicitly assumed that the *ratios* of competitors' bids to bidder's cost *are* mutually independent. This assumption is certainly much more reasonable than the assumption that the bids themselves are independent, since a major part of the dependence is presumably explainable in terms of similar costs.

but that not all of these will submit a bid on a particular issue. This means that, on a particular issue, the bidder will be opposed by one out of as many as

$$\sum_{i=0}^{N} \binom{N}{i} = 2^N$$

possible sets of competitors, and for each of these possible sets a joint distribution function may potentially be required. This number increases quite rapidly with N, which may in turn be quite large. Not only is the number of potentially required distributions quite large, but also there may be few or no past instances in which a particular combination of competitors was faced, which limits the ability to use historical data in the assessment process.

3. It is reasonable to expect the joint distribution function of competitors' bids on a particular issue to depend not only on the identity of the competitors but also on the characteristics of the issue itself: quality rating, maturity, and the like.

This last point, while appearing to compound our difficulties, may in fact provide the means of dealing with the first two. Let us suppose that the characteristics of a particular issue, say issue j, upon which the distributions of competitors' bids depend can be represented by an $r \times 1$ vector of factor levels,

$$\boldsymbol{x}_j = [x_{j1}, \cdots, x_{jr}]^t \ ,$$

and that *conditional* on $\boldsymbol{x}_j$ we are able to assess the *marginal* distribution function of each potential competitor's bid,[8] defined by

$$F_i(b_i|\boldsymbol{x}_j) \equiv Pr\{\tilde{b}_i < b_i|\boldsymbol{x}_j\} \ ,$$

for $i = 1, 2, \cdots, N$. For N large, the number of such distributions will be materially less than the 2^N joint distributions of possible *sets* of competitors.

In many cases it would be reasonable to suppose that any dependence among the competitors' bids is a consequence of their joint dependence upon $\boldsymbol{x}_j$. Given $\boldsymbol{x}_j$, therefore, the bids would be mutually independent (even though they are not independent unconditionally). Under this assumption, if we let C_j be the index set of the competitors on issue; (that is, C_j is a subset of the set of integers from 1 to N inclusive), then, given $\boldsymbol{x}_j$, the probability that the bidder will win the issue with a bid of b_0 will be given by

$$Q(b_0|\boldsymbol{x}_j) = \prod_{i \in C_j} F_i(b_0|\boldsymbol{x}_j) \ . \tag{6-8}$$

Assuming that $\boldsymbol{x}_j$ is known prior to the bidding, the objective of the bidder in this case is to maximize $(1 - b_0)Q(b_0|\boldsymbol{x}_j)$. Proceeding as in Sec. 6.1.2, we can determine that maximization of this payoff requires that the following condition be satisfied:

---

[8] A procedure for doing so will be suggested in Sec. 6.2.

$$\sum_{i \epsilon C_i} \frac{f_i(b_0|x_j)}{F_i(b_0|x_j)} - \frac{1}{1 - b_0} = 0 \ , \tag{6-9}$$

where $f_i(\cdot|x_j)$ is the marginal density function of the ith competitor's bid given x_j.

▶Condition (6-9) results from setting equal to 0 the derivative of $\log (1 - b_0)\Pi F_i(b_0|x_j)$. ◀

6.2. A Regression Model for Probability Assessment

In this section we will develop a procedure for assessing the probability distribution of $\tilde{b}_i$ based on the assumption that $\tilde{b}_i$ is generated by a Normal regression process with unknown parameters. The theory underlying this procedure was developed by Raiffa and Schlaifer.[9]

For purposes of this section, we drop the assumption that all bids are normalized by dividing by the value of winning the issue; in this section, bids will be expressed in terms of fraction of par value.

6.2.1. Process Model

We assume that $\tilde{b}_{ij}$, the bid of the ith competitor on the jth issue, is determined by the model

$$\tilde{b}_{ij} = \sum_{k=1}^{r} x_{jk}\gamma_{ik} + \epsilon_{ij} \ , \tag{6-10}$$

where the x's are defined as in the preceding section; or equivalently, if we define the vector

$$\gamma_i = [\gamma_{i1}, \cdots, \gamma_{ir}]^t \ ,$$

by

$$\tilde{b}_{ij} = x_j'\gamma_i + \tilde{\epsilon}_{ij} \ . \tag{6-11}$$

We assume that γ_i is a parameter whose value remains fixed (though possibly unknown) on all issues and that, given i, the ϵ's are independent random variables with identical Normal densities

$$f_N(\epsilon_{ij}|0, h_i) \ . \tag{6-12}$$

The parameter h_i is called the precision of the process.

Given x_j, γ_i, and h_i, therefore, $\tilde{b}_{ij}$ has the Normal density

$$f_N(b_i|x_j'\gamma_i, h_i) \ . \tag{6-13}$$

6.2.2. Distribution of Process Parameters and Marginal Distribution of the Bid

While we require that x_j be known to the bidder prior to the jth bid, in general the process parameters (γ_i, h_i) will *not* be known. To find the distribution of b_{ij} marginal with respect to these parameters, therefore, we must first assign a prob-

---

[9] *Applied Statistical Decision Theory*, Chapter 13, especially Secs. 13.5 and 13.6.

ability distribution to the parameters and then integrate them out of the joint distribution of $(\tilde{b}_{ij}, \tilde{\gamma}_i, \tilde{h}_i)$. Following the natural conjugate theory of Raiffa and Schlaifer, we will assign to $(\tilde{\gamma}_i, \tilde{h}_i)$ the Normal-gamma density

$$f^{(r)}_{n\gamma}(\gamma_i, h_i | g'_i, v'_i, \mathbf{n}'_i, \nu'_i) \ . \tag{6-14}$$

Integrating the distribution of $(\tilde{b}_{ij}, \tilde{\gamma}_i, \tilde{h}_i)$ with respect to $(\tilde{\gamma}_i, \tilde{h}_i)$, we determine that, marginally, the bid $\tilde{b}_{ij}$ has the Student density[10]

$$f_S(b_{ij} | \mathbf{x}'_j g'_i, n_b/v'_i, \nu'_i) \ , \tag{6-15a}$$

where

$$n_b = (\mathbf{x}'_j \mathbf{n}'_i \mathbf{x}_j + 1)^{-1} \ . \tag{6-15b}$$

For calculating the optimal bid, we require the ratio f_i/F_i of ordinate to the left tail of the marginal distribution. Bracken and Schleifer[11] have tabulated the ordinates and the *right* tails of the *standardized* Student distribution, that is

$$f_{S*}(t|\nu) \quad \text{and} \quad G_{S*}(t|\nu) = 1 - F_{S*}(t|\nu) \ ,$$

for various values of the argument t and the parameter ν. Defining

$$t_i = (n_b/v'_i)^{1/2}(b_i - \mathbf{x}'_j g'_i) \ , \tag{6-16}$$

the required ratio can be obtained from the Bracken-Schleifer tables as follows:

$$\frac{f_i(b_i | \mathbf{x}_j)}{F_i(b_i | \mathbf{x}_j)} = \left(\frac{n_b}{v'_i}\right)^{1/2} \left(\frac{f_{S*}(t_i | \nu'_i)}{1 - G_{S*}(t_i | \nu'_i)}\right) \ . \tag{6-17}$$

6.2.3. *Prior-Posterior Analysis and Updating of Distributions*

In assessing his distribution of $(\tilde{\gamma}_i, \tilde{h}_i)$, and therefore his distribution of b_{ij} given $\mathbf{x}_j$, the bidder will wish to consider any information which can be gleaned from the previous bidding history of the ith competitor. Moreover, following the jth issue, the bidder will wish to use data on that issue to update his distributions. Both of these requirements can be met through the prior-posterior theory developed by Raiffa and Schlaifer.[12]

To simplify the notation somewhat, in the remainder of this section, we will suppress the subscript i.

Reparametrization of distribution of $(\tilde{\gamma}, \tilde{h})$. Updating of the distributions after each observation will be facilitated by a slight change in the parameters of the distribution of $(\tilde{\gamma}, \tilde{h})$. Rather than the standard parameters $(g', v', \mathbf{n}', \nu')$ employed earlier, it will be convenient to use new parameters defined in terms of the standard parameters as follows:

$$\mathbf{n}' \tag{6-18a}$$

$$s'_{xb} = \mathbf{n}'g' \ , \qquad \text{an } r \times 1 \text{ vector} \ , \tag{6-18b}$$

$$s'_b = v'\nu' + g'^t\mathbf{n}'g' \ , \qquad \text{a scalar} \ , \tag{6-18c}$$

$$n' = \nu' + \min(n', r) \ . \tag{6-18d}$$

---

[10] This result is the specialization to the case of a single observation of that given in Raiffa and Schlaifer, *op. cit.*, Sec. 13.6.1.

[11] *Tables for Normal Sampling with Unknown Variance.*

[12] *Op. cit.*, Sec. 13.5.2.

This transformation of parameters always exists, but the inverse transformation back to the standard parameters exists only if $\mathbf{n}'$ is of full rank and $\nu' > 0$. If the inverse transformation does not exist, then the distribution of $(\tilde{\gamma}, \tilde{h})$ is not a proper distribution (i.e., its integral over its range does not converge).

Sample statistics. If the bidder has observed n previous bids by a competitor, the data on these observations can be represented by the number n, the vector

$$\boldsymbol{b} = [b_1, \cdots, b_l, \cdots, b_n]^t \tag{6-19a}$$

and the matrix

$$\mathbf{X} = \begin{bmatrix} \boldsymbol{x}_1' \\ \cdots \\ \boldsymbol{x}_l' \\ \cdots \\ \boldsymbol{x}_n' \end{bmatrix} = \begin{bmatrix} x_{11} & \cdots & x_{1k} & \cdots & x_{1r} \\ \cdots & \cdots & \cdots & \cdots & \cdots \\ x_{l1} & \cdots & x_{lk} & \cdots & x_{lr} \\ \cdots & \cdots & \cdots & \cdots & \cdots \\ x_{n1} & \cdots & x_{nk} & \cdots & x_{nr} \end{bmatrix} . \tag{6-19b}$$

From these data we can compute the statistics (sums of squares and cross products).

$$\mathbf{n} = \mathbf{X}^t\mathbf{X} , \tag{6-20a}$$

$$\boldsymbol{s}_{xb} = \mathbf{X}^t\boldsymbol{b} , \tag{6-20b}$$

$$s_b = \boldsymbol{b}^t\boldsymbol{b} . \tag{6-20c}$$

Posterior parameters. If, prior to the observations on previous bids, the bidder had assigned to $(\tilde{\gamma}, \tilde{h})$ a Normal-gamma distribution with (transformed) parameters (6-18); and if n previous observations have resulted in the statistics (6-20), then, as Raiffa and Schlaifer have shown, posterior to the observations the distribution of (γ, h) will be Normal-gamma with parameters

$$\mathbf{n}'' = \mathbf{n}' + \mathbf{n} , \tag{6-21a}$$

$$\boldsymbol{s}_{xb}'' = \boldsymbol{s}_{xb}' + \boldsymbol{s}_{xb} , \tag{6-21b}$$

$$s_b'' = s_b' + s_b , \tag{6-21c}$$

$$n'' = n' + n . \tag{6-21d}$$

Provided that $\mathbf{n}''$ is of full rank and that $\nu'' > 0$, the transformation defined by (6-18) can then be inverted to provide the posterior parameters in standard form. The standard parameters can then be substituted into (6-15) to obtain the distribution of the next bid once the vector $\boldsymbol{x}$ is known for it.

Updating. Updating of distributions is readily accomplished by maintaining, for each competitor, a file containing the most recently calculated values of $(\mathbf{n}'', \boldsymbol{s}_{xb}'', s_b'', n'')$. Every time a competitor submits a bid on a new issue, the statistics (6-18) are calculated for his bid. (Note that since $n = 1$ will usually be less than r, ordinary least squares analysis of the observation is not possible, but this is of no consequence.) Then, considering the parameters in the file to be single-primed since they are prior to the new observation, the new posterior parameters are computed by simple addition, as in (6-21), and are ready to be used in obtaining the distribution of the next bid.

Computer program. A FORTRAN computer program capable of handling all of the requirements of this section, and with considerable flexibility for other applications, has been prepared by members of the staff of the Harvard Business School and is available on application to the author.

6.3. Application of the Regression Model

In this section we will present an illustrative application of the regression model developed in the previous section. Given limitations in the data available to the author, it was necessary to make some compromises in this application which would not be required of a real-world bidder. Hence the statistical results in this section should be considered as illustrative only and should not be used in practical applications without the modifications suggested at the end of the section.

6.3.1. Specification of the Model

To complete the specification of the model of competitors' behavior presented in Sec. 6.2.1, we must decide what explanatory variables are to be represented by the vector x_j. In the research reported in this monograph, two possible specifications were used, which will be discussed below. Analysis of the statistical results, however, indicates that further improvement is possible along lines to be discussed in Sec. 6.3.5.

Specification I. In Chapters 2 and 3 we observed that it is the normal practice of bidding groups to arrive at a bid by first determining public offering price and spread. Letting $\tilde{p}_{ij}$ be the ith competitor's contemplated offering price on the jth issue and $\tilde{s}_{ij}$ be his desired spread, then his bid will be

$$\tilde{b}_{ij} = \tilde{p}_{ij} - \tilde{s}_{ij} .\qquad(6\text{-}22)$$

It seems reasonable to assume that $\tilde{p}_{ij}$ is closely related to the bidder's own contemplated offering price. Both the bidder and his competitors expect to sell the bonds in the same final market and have similar information about this market. Letting x_{j2} represent the bidder's offering price, we postulate the following relationship:

$$\tilde{p}_{ij} = \gamma_{i2} x_{j2} + \tilde{u}_{ij} ,\qquad(6\text{-}23)$$

where $\tilde{u}_{ij}$ is assumed to be a Normal variate with 0 mean. (It might be reasonable to assume a multiplicative error term, but since in practice x_{j2} will be quite close to 1 the additive assumption is at least a good approximation.)

The coefficient γ_{i2} in (6-23) may be interpreted as a measure of the "pricing bias" of the competitor: it indicates the extent to which he typically prices above ($\gamma_{i2} > 1$) or below ($\gamma_{i2} < 1$) the bidder.

We will assume that the competitor's spread $\tilde{s}_{ij}$ can likewise be explained as a linear combination of explanatory variables. Cohan has argued that, on the average, two variables suffice to explain spread: *yield* and *time*. All other factors

81

influencing spread appear to be related to one or both of these. Quality rating, for example, is inversely associated with yield.[13]

Since the public offering price is generally close to 100, as a measure of contemplated yield on an issue we will use the bidder's own coupon rate, which we will denote by x_{j4}. Time, measured in years since 1900, will be denoted by x_{j3}. Our explanatory equation will be:

$$-\tilde{s}_{ij} = \gamma_{j1} + \gamma_{j3}x_{j3} + \gamma_{j4}x_{j4} + \tilde{w}_{ij} \qquad (6\text{-}24)$$

where $\tilde{w}_{ij}$ is assumed to be a Normal variate with 0 mean. (We explain $-\tilde{s}_{ij}$ because spread enters into equation (6-22) with negative sign.)

The constant term γ_{j1} in (6-24) can be interpreted as a "base spread" from which deviations are explained by the remaining terms.

We see, therefore, that by substitution of (6-23) and (6-24) into (6-22), we obtain a specification of the basic model where

$\qquad x_{j1}$ is a constant 1 ,
$\qquad x_{j2}$ is the bidder's contemplated offering price ,
$\qquad x_{j3}$ is time in years since 1900 ,
$\qquad x_{j4}$ is the bidder's contemplated coupon ,
$\qquad \tilde{\epsilon}_{ij}$ is $\tilde{u}_{ij} + \tilde{w}_{ij}$, a Normal variate with 0 mean .

Specification II. When prior-posterior analysis was done using Specification I, the results were not considered entirely satisfactory, particularly with respect to the size of the posterior variance parameter v_i''. Accordingly, when the analysis was repeated using augmented data, as discussed below, a modified specification was used. The changes were entirely in the variables explaining spread. The new specification used the following variables:

$\qquad x_{j1}$ a constant 1,
$\qquad x_{j2}$ the bidder's contemplated offering price,
$\qquad x_{j3}$ the bidder's contemplated coupon divided by the value for the previous week of Moody's index of yields on A-rated public utility bonds,
$\qquad x_{j4}$ the change in the previous week of Moody's index of yields on A-rated public utility bonds,
$\qquad x_{j5}$ the reciprocal of the size of the issue, where size is expressed in thousands of dollars of par value,
$\qquad x_{j6}$ time in years since 1900.

The variables x_{j3} and x_{j4} in Specification II take the place of the coupon rate in Specification I, while x_{j5} is intended to reflect the influence of fixed costs on the size of the spread.

6.3.2. *Data Employed*

For the application of the prior-posterior theory developed in Section 6.2, a convenient source of data was at hand in the form of the Public Sealed Bidding

---

[13] A. B. Cohan, *Cost of Flotation of Long-Term Corporate Debt Since 1935.*

(PSB) Sheets prepared by counsel for the defendants in the case *U.S.* v. *Morgan, et al.* For all issues offered at public sealed bidding during the period January 1, 1935, to December 31, 1949, these sheets contain descriptive information about the issue and identify the managers of bidding groups.

A preliminary selection was made from the PSB Sheets of debt issues of public utility companies issued subsequent to January 1, 1941. This date was chosen since, prior to the promulgation of Rule U-50 by the SEC in 1941, the quantity of debt sold at competitive bidding was negligible.

The preliminary selection included a total of 364 issues. For only about one-third of these (122 issues), however, did the public sealed bidding sheets contain sufficient data on the explanatory variables to use in applying the model of Section 6.2. The excluded cases included the great bulk of issues in the years 1947–1949, so that for all practical purposes the data were restricted to the period 1941–1946. These restricted data were used for the prior-posterior analysis of Specification I.

For the analysis of Specification II, on the other hand, additional research was done which resulted in obtaining complete data on an additional 207 of the issues for which there were PSB Sheets. This left only 35 issues with incomplete data in the 1941–1949 time period. In addition, a complete catalog of issues offered at public sealed bidding from January 1, 1950, to May 31, 1958, was obtained from Halsey, Stuart & Co. Inc.[14] By the time the computer analysis of Specification II was run, however, it had been possible to complete compilation of data only on 52 issues offered in 1951. Thus, the total Specification II sample consisted of 381 issues.

Each of the included issues, both in the Specification I and Specification II samples, was bid on by one or more bidding groups. In some cases, a bidding group submitted more than one bid on an issue. These were generally cases in which an issuer offered two classes of securities (e.g., bonds and common stock) at the same time; in these cases, some bidders would submit one bid for the bonds alone and a second bid for the bonds and the other class of securities combined. Bids of the second kind (so-called "basket bids") were deleted from the sample, leaving 473 separate observations in the Specification I sample and 1,837 in the Specification II sample.

Of course, not every investment banking firm managed a bidding group on each of the 381 Specification II issues. The most active manager was Halsey, Stuart & Co. Inc., which managed groups bidding on 348 issues. Some firms appeared as managers only a single time.

6.3.3.   Problems in Measurement and Data Interpretation

Very rarely are any two bidding groups identical. The manager may vary the list of those he invites to participate, he may encounter refusals by those he

---

[14] *Competitive Sales and Negotiated Public Offerings of New Public Utility, Railroad, and Industrial Debt Issues.*

invites, and some participants may drop out at the final price meeting. This raises the problem of defining a competitor. For our purposes, we decided to identify each bidding group with its manager, ignoring the internal composition of the group. While this composition undoubtedly has some influence on the group's bidding behavior, this influence is probably of second-order importance relative to that of the manager (who, after all, selects his associates).

A second difficulty is encountered in measuring the *bidder's* public offering price. The only public offering price which is customarily announced is that of the *winner*, while the price included in the model is intended to be that of a particular bidding group which may or may not be the winner. Nevertheless, the public offering price of the winner was used as the best available measure of the offering price of the bidder. The same convention was adopted with respect to the coupon rate. This is the most important convention limiting the applicability of the results to real bidding situations.

On a number of issues, different coupon rates were stipulated by some of the bidding groups, rendering their dollar bid prices noncomparable. Comparability was restored by first calculating the cost of money implied by each bid-coupon combination and then converting this cost of money into a "standardized" bid using the coupon rate stipulated by the winning bidder. That is, the standardized bid for each bidding group was the dollar bid it would have submitted had it adopted the winning bidder's coupon but its own cost of money.

6.3.4. Sample Statistics

For the Specification I case, a separate least-squares regression analysis was performed for each investment banking firm which had managed groups bidding on at least 5 of the 122 issues; there were 18 such firms. The Harvard Computation Center's standard multiple regression program was used; the restriction to firms bidding on at least five issues was imposed since that program was not suitable for sample x's of less than full rank. In addition, that program did not provide the matrix n^{-1} as output, so that a separate matrix inversion routine was used to obtain that inverse.

For the Specification II case, the Bayes regression program mentioned in Section 6.2.3 was used. Since this program was designed to be used with samples of any size, all managers were included in the analysis. All desired outputs were provided by the program. While this program will accept prior parameters as input, none were provided in the present analysis.

The results of the statistical analysis are presented in Tables 6.1 and 6.2 for the two managing firms with the greatest number of managerships: First Boston Corporation and Halsey, Stuart & Company, Inc. Results for other managers may be obtained on request to the author. Specification I results are given in Table 6.1 and Specification II results in Table 6.2. In each case, the order of the variables is that specified in Sec. 6.3.1. Only below-diagonal elements are shown for the matrices n and n^{-1}, which are symmetric. Floating point notation has been

Table 6.1

Sample Statistics: Specification I

---

a. *First Boston Corporation*

n	66.0			
	6788.9243	698712.7031		
	2933.0000	301582.	130529.0000	
	202.9750	20897.	9000.0000	631.0319
$(\mathbf{X'b})^t$	6707.1431	690294.	297975.	20641.
$b'b$	682004.8125			
n	66			
$\mathbf{n}^{-1}$	0.729398E 02			
	−0.381878E − 00	0.310156E − 02		
	−0.645680E 00	0.158205E − 02	0.911280E − 02	
	−0.160941E 01	−0.242512E − 02	0.253531E − 01	0.238051E 00
g^t	−9.1249	1.0407	0.1154	−0.4659

b. *Halsey, Stuart & Company, Inc.*

n	107.0			
	11005.3035	1132436.2812		
	4770.0000	490045.	212866.0000	
	323.1000	33259.	14379.	985.6725
$(\mathbf{X'b})^t$	10849.5148	1116360.	483571.	32777.
$b'b$	1100650.5781			
n	107			
$\mathbf{n}^{-1}$	0.587478E 02	E 02		
	−0.331269E 00	0.264538E − 02		
	−0.510168E 00	0.154732E − 02	0.701858E − 02	
	−0.636963E 00	−0.324577E − 02	0.126296E − 01	0.135044E 00
g^t	−9.6622	1.0037	0.2234	−0.7042

---

used wherever a number is followed by an E; the number following the E then represents the power of 10 by which the preceding number must be multiplied.

6.3.5. *Illustrative Computation of Optimal Bid*

To illustrate the use of the regression model in calculating the optimal bid, let us assume that the bidder is competing against groups managed by First Boston

Table 6.2
Sample Statistics: Specification II

a. First Boston Corporation

n

0.224000E 03	0.232624E 07	0.250965E 03	0.923060E −01	0.664686E −05	0.504515E 06
0.228242E 05	0.241112E 05	0.594619E 00	0.151646E −04	0.130806E 01	
0.236539E 03	0.553314E 02	0.294002E −01	0.271520E 02		
0.544000E 00	0.281473E 01	0.111984E 05			
0.276293E −01	0.108143E 07				
0.106170E 05					

$(X^t b)^t$

0.226046E 05	0.230380E 07	0.238762E 05	0.546434E 02	0.278410E 01	0.107100E 07

$b^t b$ 0.228171E 07

n 224

n^{-1}

0.292030E 02	0.217163E −02	0.103720E 01	0.114382E 02	0.317430E 06	0.101073E −02
−0.233641E 00	−0.117002E −01	−0.395715E 00	0.202936E 03	−0.216906E 00	
−0.237392E 00	−0.205913E −02	−0.766958E 02	−0.163688E −01		
0.135071E 01	0.136655E 01	0.727299E −02			
−0.876187E 02	0.518116E −03				
−0.108312E 00					

g^t

0.162402E 02	0.885527E 00	−0.230884E 01	−0.828369E 00	−0.995531E 03	−0.697937E −01

b. Halsey, Stuart & Company, Inc.

n

0.348000E 03	0.361956E 07	0.393278E 03	0.142857E 00	0.910234E −05	0.786564E 06
0.354869E 05	0.376213E 05	0.820794E 00	0.916127E −04	0.197042E 01	
0.368798E 03	0.739302E 02	0.440569E −01	0.364450E 02		
0.723000E 00	0.420527E 01	0.175015E 05			
0.412579E −01	0.168447E 07				
0.165240E 05					

$(X^t b)^t$

0.351683E 05	0.358692E 07	0.372754E 05	0.724281E 02	0.416409E 01	0.166939E 07

$b^t b$ 0.355479E 07

n 348

n^{-1}

0.213920E 02	0.161786E −02	0.462810E 00	0.730968E 01	0.245406E 06	0.652056E −03
−0.177329E 00	−0.710384E −02	0.179434E 00	0.303145E 02	−0.162129E 01	
0.199050E 00	−0.584860E −02	−0.429694E 02	−0.106175E −01		
0.127193E 01	0.208844E 00	0.849936E −03			
0.720664E 00	0.413846E −03				
−0.743083E −01					

g^t

0.190322E 02	0.840714E 00	−0.239159E 01	−0.442236E 01	−0.621688E 00	−0.229492E −01

Corporation and Halsey, Stuart & Co. Inc., respectively, on an issue with the following characteristics:

Bidder's contemplated offering price	100
Bidder's contemplated coupon divided by Moody's index	1
Previous week's change in Moody's index	.01
Par value of issue (thousands)	10,000
Year	1950

Thus, $x^t = [1, 10^2, 1, 10^{-2}, 10^{-4}, .5 \times 10^2]$.

We will further assume that the bidder has expected selling and inventory costs of 40¢ per \$100 of par value, so that the value to him of winning the bid is 99.60% of par value.

We will assume that the bidder's prior (non-sample) information about the bidding behavior of his competitors is negligible in comparison with the sample information;[15] we will, therefore, assume that the posterior parameters are equal to the corresponding sample statistics.[16] The statistics for the Specification II model will be used.

First we must calculate the parameters of the distribution (6-15) of the competitors' bids. These parameters are listed in Table 6.3. The table also lists the critical values of t, defined by (6-16), and of the ratio (6-17).

Because the number of degrees of freedom, ν, in the two distributions is so large, the Normal approximation to the Student distribution was used. Using the iterative procedure suggested in Sec. 6.1.3, the optimal bid b^* was determined to be 98.52. The probability of winning with this bid was determined to be .129, and the expected payoff to the bidder is, therefore, $.129 \times (99.6 - 98.52) = 0.139\%$ of par value.

Table 6.3

Parameters of Illustrative Distributions

	First Boston	Halsey, Stuart
$x^t g$	99.186566	99.458137
n_b/ν	.202226	.200337
ν	218	342
t	$.44969b_0 - 44.60321$	$.44759b_0 - 44.51647$
f/F	$\dfrac{.44969 f_{S*}(t\|218)}{1 - G_{S*}(t\|218)}$	$\dfrac{.44759 f_{S*}(t\|342)}{1 - G_{S*}(t\|342)}$

The calculated optimal bid of 98.52 is probably considerably less than a bidder not using the regression model would actually submit on an issue like the hypo-

---

[15] This is reasonable in the case of First Boston Corporation and Halsey, Stuart, on whom the sample evidence is considerable, but would not be acceptable in the case of managers on whom there is little sample evidence.

[16] See Raiffa and Schlaifer, *op. cit.*

thetical one used in our example. This is not necessarily evidence of irrational behavior, however; it may be that the bidder's subjective uncertainty about competitors' bids is considerably less than postulated by our model. This is an aspect of the problem which requires further research.

6.3.6. *Suggestions for Further Improvement of the Model*

While the Specification II model appears to be more satisfactory than the Specification I model in most respects, there is still some evidence that further research and possible improvement in the structure of the model are desirable. Some of the parameter estimates are considerably different from values that might have been estimated *a priori*. For example, the coefficient of public offering price should be near 1 according to the interpretation of the model, but is 10% to 15% away in the data given in Table 6.2. In this respect, in fact, although not in others, Specification I turns out to give results more in accordance with the interpretation.

One promising approach to meeting the objective just raised is to assign a prior distribution to the coefficient of public offering price with a mean close to 1 and with a small variance. If the mean is set equal to 1 and the variance equal to 0, this would be equivalent to a model which explained $b_{ij} - x_{j2}$, the *difference* between the competitor's bid and the public offering price rather than the bid itself. While this approach was not carried out to any extent, some test calculations on simulated data indicated that it resulted in an improved specification. Further effort would also be desirable in experimenting with other specifications, possibly involving only transformations of the Specification II variables.

6.4. A Final Problem

Suppose that it is known by all competitors that a bidder is following the bidding system developed in this chapter, and suppose further that these competitors also know the composition of the sample of observations used by the bidder in determining *his* probability distribution of *their* bids. Under these circumstances, the *competitors* will have probability distributions of the *bidder's* bid in which the only elements contributing to their uncertainty is their lack of knowledge of x^t, or specifically of the bidder's proposed offering price and coupon.

If, then, these competitors bid optimally according to the probability distributions described in the preceding paragraph, *the bidder's bid determined according to the method of this chapter will no longer be optimal.* To show this, we need only consider the extreme case in which the competitors know x^t with certainty. In the example of Sec. 6.3.5, for instance, if Halsey, Stuart and First Boston knew x^t with certainty, they would also know with certainty that our hypothetical bidder would bid 98.52. They would optimize their own returns, then, by bidding the next admissible bid over 98.52 (assuming they valued winning the bid at more than 98.52).

It will be recognized that the difficulty we are describing here is that the statistical bidding model does not, in the language of game theory, result in equilibrium bids. One conclusion is that it is advantageous to a bidder using the model to keep his use of it secret. Whether this is possible in investment banking, with the fluidity of its syndicates, is dubious.

This point also raises a matter for further research. What would be the time pattern of behavior of a market in which all bidders used the model of this chapter? It is conjectured that bids would converge to equilibrium-type solutions, although the presence of uncertainty militates against a strict application of the equilibrium-point concept of game theory.

CHAPTER 7

The Group Decision Process

In Chapters 3 through 6 we have assumed that the goal of each bidder is to maximize the expected value of some objective function. If each bidder were a single person, this assumption could be justified by reference to the theory of rational individual decision making under uncertainty, which is summarized below in Sec. 7.1.2. Bids are, however, normally submitted by syndicates of investment banking firms. Even disregarding the fact that each such firm comprises a number of individual partners, stockholders, or officers, we must face up to the question of whether or not principles of choice which are appropriate to individual behavior also apply when the decision maker is a group.

In this chapter we will consider two separate approaches to the resolution of the group decision process. In Sec. 7.1 we will examine assumptions under which it can be concluded that a group "ought" to maximize expected utility, i.e., represent its preference among acts by a real-valued preference function for which the operation of expectation is defined. In Sec. 7.2 quite a different point of view will be taken: we will consider the group decision process as a sort of non-cooperative [sic] game. This formulation of the process appears to be descriptively superior to the "cooperative" formulation of Sec. 7.1 when applied to the bidding situation, but it lacks some of the normatively desirable features of the latter approach.

7.1. A Group as a Maximizer of Expected Utility

7.1.1. Basic Notation

Throughout this section we will assume that the decision maker, whether an individual or a group, can specify the following elements of his decision problem:

1. *Act space:* $A = \{a\}$.

The decision maker wishes to select a single act a from some domain of potential acts.

2. *State space:* $\Theta = \{\theta\}$.

The decision maker believes that the consequence of adopting an act a depends on some "state of the world" θ which he cannot predict with certainty. We will assume that the domain of θ, or Θ, is finite.

3. *Consequences:* $C = \{c\}$.

Corresponding to each $(a, \theta) \, \epsilon \, A \times \Theta$, there will be an identifiable consequence c to the decision maker; the domain of c will be denoted by C. Formally, a is a function from Θ to C; that is, $c = a(\theta)$. In much of this section, we will suppress reference to C and adopt the ellipsis of referring to the ordered pair (a, θ) as a "consequence."

7.1.2. *Individual Decision Making Under Uncertainty*

Since a decision-making group is composed of individuals, before proceeding with our examination of the group decision process let us first summarize briefly the theory of rational behavior under uncertainty for individual decision makers.[1] So that we may extend this discussion to the group context, we will assume that our discussion applies to an individual decision maker, j, who may be a member of a group, although for the time being we will consider only his behavior in individual choice problems.

We make the following assumptions about the decision maker:

1a. The decision maker *can imagine* an experiment all of whose outcomes are "equally likely" in the sense that *he* would be *indifferent* between any two lotteries one of which entitles him to a certain valuable prize if some one, particular outcome occurs while the other entitles him to that *same* prize if some other one, particular outcome occurs.

1b. As regards any two lotteries one of which entitles him to a valuable prize if *any one* of n_1 particular outcomes of the experiment of 1a occurs while the other entitles him to that same prize if any one of n_2 particular outcomes occurs, he will prefer the former lottery to the latter if and only if n_1 is greater than n_2.

If an experiment has N "equally likely" outcomes, we say that the *canonical chance* that some one of any n particular outcomes will occur is n/N.

2. The decision maker can select reference consequences c^* and c_* such that c^* is *at least* as attractive as any possible consequence of any of the available acts and c_* is *at least* as unattractive as any possible consequence of any of the available acts; and he can then:

    a. Scale his *preference* for any possible *consequence* c by specifying a number $\pi_j(c)$ such that *he* would be *indifferent* between (1) c for certain, and (2) a lottery giving a canonical chance $\pi_j(c)$ at c^* and a complementary chance at c_*;

    b. Scale his *judgment* concerning any possible *event* θ by specifying a number $P_j(\theta)$ such that *he* would be *indifferent* between (1) a lottery

---

[1] Savage, in *The Foundations of Statistics*, presents the most complete discussion of this theory, as well as an intellectual history and bibliography. A recent, more elementary treatment is given by Pratt, Raiffa, and Schlaifer, "The Foundations of Decision Under Uncertainty: An Elementary Exposition," *Journal of the American Statistical Association, 59*, pp. 353–375 (1964). The assumptions and conclusions stated in the text above are a slight paraphrase of those given in the latter source.

with consequence c^* if θ occurs, c_* if it does not, and (2) a lottery giving a canonical chance $P_j(\theta)$ at c^* and a complementary chance at c_*.

3. As regards any set of lotteries among which the decision maker has evaluated his feelings of preference or indifference, these relations should be *transitive*. If, for example, he prefers lottery A to lottery B and is indifferent between lottery B and lottery C, then he should prefer lottery A to lottery C.

4. If some of the prizes in a lottery are replaced by other prizes such that the decision maker is indifferent between each new prize and the corresponding original prize, then the decision maker should be indifferent between the original and the modified lotteries.

Given these assumptions, it can be proven that the decision maker's preference among acts should be governed by the index

$$\Pi_j(a) \equiv \sum_{\theta \in \Theta} P_j(\theta)\pi_j[a(\theta)] \; ; \tag{7-1}$$

that is, if a' and a'' are any two acts, the decision maker should prefer a' to a'' if and only if $\Pi_j(a')$ is greater than $\Pi_j(a'')$.

It can also be shown that the scaled judgments $P_j(\theta)$ obey the axioms of the mathematical theory of probability; for this reason they are generally referred to as *personal* or *subjective probabilities*. The scaled preferences $\pi_j(c) = \pi_j[a(\theta)]$ are generally called *utilities*. While the scaled judgments are determined uniquely, the scaled preferences are determined only up to a positive linear transformation in the sense that the decision maker's preferences among acts could be expressed equally well by the index

$$\bar{u}_j(a) \equiv \sum_{\theta \in \Theta} P_j(\theta)u_j(a, \theta) \; , \tag{7-2}$$

where

$$u_j(a, \theta) \equiv \alpha_j + \beta_j\pi_j[a(\theta)] \; , \qquad \begin{matrix} \alpha_j \text{ and } \beta_j \text{ real } , \\ \beta_j > 0 \; . \end{matrix} \tag{7-3}$$

We can state our conclusion in another way: given the assumptions of the theory of individual decision making under uncertainty, the objective of the decision maker is to maximize the expected value of the function $u_j(a, \theta)$ defined by (7-3).

From this discussion, it can be seen that there are three basic reasons why the members of a group might not be able to agree on their preference ordering of group acts.

First of all, even if the decision is made under certainty, the members of the group may differ in their rank-ordering of the outcomes. This is particularly likely to be the case where an act determines, among other things, the division of the joint proceeds among the participants. Presumably each member would like his share to be as large as possible, but in general it may be increased only at the expense of other members of the group.

If the decision is made under risk (i.e., with an "objective" or common probability distribution given) the members of the group may disagree on acts even though they agree on the rank-ordering of outcomes. The disagreement may arise because of differences in attitudes toward assuming risk, as reflected in choices among randomized acts. In order for unanimity to be reached under risk, the members of a group must agree not only on their rank-ordering of outcomes, but also on their rank-ordering of all probability distributions of outcomes; i.e., they must have identical preference functions.

Finally, even if the members of the group do have identical rank-orderings of probability distributions, they might still disagree on the choice of acts in a decision problem under uncertainty. In this case the disagreement would arise from differences in the personal probabilities assigned to the states of the world by each act.

Each of the three sources of disagreement just outlined (ranking of outcomes, attitude toward risk, and differences in probabilities) may and probably does occur in a competitive bidding situation. First, if the deal is expected to be a good one by almost everyone in a bidding group, many of the members may wish to increase their participations, but this cannot be done without reducing the participation of other equally eager participants; this is a disagreement about outcomes. Second, some investment banking firms may be more willing than others to speculate on a possible market upturn, even though there is general agreement on the probability of such an upturn. Because of an abundance of capital, a propensity toward risk-taking on the part of their leading personnel, and so forth, these firms may be more disposed to take a risk than the others. Finally, each investment banking firm has its own sources of information, and these differences in sources are likely to lead to differences in expectations as to the price at which the bonds can be sold. (An important function of the price meeting, in fact, is to attempt to reconcile these informational differences.)

7.1.3. Group Preference—Formal Development

We will now proceed to develop conditions on group preference which will be sufficient to enable us to conclude that a group should also seek to maximize the expected value of some objective function.[2]

We assume that there are N members in a group and that the preferences of each individual member of the group satisfy the assumptions and hence the conclusions of Sec. 7.1.3; that is, the preferences of member j for consequences are represented by the function defined by (7-3) and those for acts by the function defined by (7-2). We further assume that the relative evaluation by the group of any two acts a' and a'' will depend solely on the numbers $[\bar{u}_j(a')]$ and $[\bar{u}_j(a'')]$ respectively.

For a', $a'' \in A$ and $0 \leq \lambda \leq 1$, we define $\lambda a' + (1 - \lambda)a''$ as a *mixed act* whereby the group chooses a' with probability λ and a'' with probability $(1 - \lambda)$, and we assume that A includes all such acts. The preference of the jth group member for such an act is, by virtue of the preceding section, measured by

$$\lambda \bar{u}_j(a') + (1 - \lambda)\bar{u}_j(a'') \ .$$

[2] The relationship of our approach to others in the literature will be discussed in Sec. 7.1.7.

We further assume the existence of a binary relation $\geq$ on $A \times A$, which is to be interpreted as follows: $a' \geq a''$ means that the group does not prefer a'' to a'. We assume that there are at least two elements of A such that the group is not indifferent between them. Finally, we assume that the relation $\geq$ satisfies the following axioms.

Axiom 1 (Comparability).   For any a', $a'' \epsilon A$, either $a' \geq a''$ or $a'' \geq a'$.

This axiom asserts that the group is capable of deciding which of any pair of acts it prefers or that it is indifferent between them.

Axiom 2 (Transitivity).   For any a', a'', and $a''' \epsilon A$, if $a' \geq a''$ and $a'' \geq a'''$, then $a' \geq a'''$.

As is now well known, some apparently reasonable social decision procedures violate this axiom. Consider, for example, a three-person, three-act decision problem with the following individual preference indices:

$$\overline{u}_1(a') > \overline{u}_1(a'') > \overline{u}_1(a''') \;;$$
$$\overline{u}_2(a'') > \overline{u}_2(a''') > \overline{u}_2(a') \;;$$
$$\overline{u}_3(a''') > \overline{u}_3(a') > \overline{u}_3(a'') \;.$$

Member 1, for example, prefers a' to a'' to a'''. Now adopt the following group decision procedure (majority rule): the group will choose one act in preference to another if a majority of the group prefers the first act. Then, in the example, the group will choose a' over a'', a'' over a''', and a''' over a', in violation of Axiom 2.

The fact that actual decision procedures may result in intransitivities does not necessarily argue against Axiom 2, of course.[3]   And on the other hand, if a group does actually prefer a' to a'', a'' to a''', and a''' to a', this implies that if it is committed to performing a', it should be willing to pay a premium to be relieved of this commitment and permitted to perform a'''; but then it should be willing to pay another premium to substitute a'' for a'''; and another one to substitute a' for a''; and so on indefinitely.

Axiom 3 (Substitutability).   For any a', a'', and $a''' \epsilon A$ and for $0 \leq \lambda \leq 1$, if $a' \geq a''$, then

$$\lambda a' + (1 - \lambda)a''' \geq \lambda a'' + (1 - \lambda)a''' \;.$$

This axiom implies that group preference for acts should not be affected by a change in the origin of measurement of the individual utility functions. Since, as we stated in Sec. 7.1.2, this origin is arbitrary, Axiom 3 would appear to be quite innocuous, and its equivalent is included in virtually all discussions of the group decision problem (see Sec. 7.1.7). However, the following counterexample might appeal to some: Consider a group with two members, and let the individual utilities be as given at the top of the following page.

---

[3] The method of majority rule will not violate Axiom 2 if individual preferences are subjected to an appropriate condition (Single-Peakedness); see K. J. Arrow, *Social Choice and Individual Values*, pp. 75–80.

	a'	a''	a'''	$\frac{1}{2}a' + \frac{1}{2}a'''$	$\frac{1}{2}a'' + \frac{1}{2}a'''$
Member 1	.5	.0	.5	.5	.25
Member 2	.5	1.0	$-.5$	.0	.25

It might be the case that the group would prefer to have both members do moderately well than to have one do very well and the other do very poorly, and so the group preference would be $a' \gtrsim a''$ but $\frac{1}{2}a'' + \frac{1}{2}a''' \gtrsim \frac{1}{2}a' + \frac{1}{2}a'''$. But this violates Axiom 3.

Defenders of the axiom would argue that both mixed acts lead to a''' with the same probability, so that the choice between them should depend only on what act will be chosen if a''' is *not* chosen; hence the group preference for a' over a'' should control.

Axiom 4 (Dominance). If $\bar{u}_j(a') \geq \bar{u}_j(a'')$ for all j, then $a' \gtrsim a''$.

This axiom says that if every member of the group considers a' at least as good as a'', then the group as a whole considers a' at least as good as a''.

Axiom 4 almost, but not quite, has the effect of requiring that the act most preferred by the group be *Pareto optimal*. Let $A_0 \subset A$; A_0 is said to be the Pareto optimal set if, for every $a \notin A_0$ there exists an $a \in A_0$ which is considered at least as good by all group members and definitely better by others.

Suppose, for example, that a' is definitely preferred by the group to any other act. If a' is *not* Pareto optimal, then there is another act a'' such that $\bar{u}_j(a'') \geq \bar{u}_j(a')$ for all j and $\bar{u}_j(a'') > \bar{u}_j(a')$ for some j. But then, by Axiom 4, it must be the case that $a'' \gtrsim a'$, contradicting the assumption that a' is the unique optimal act. Hence, if a' is the unique optimal act, it must be Pareto optimal.

If there is a most preferred act which is *not* unique, on the other hand, it is possible under Axiom 4 that some of the acts in the most preferred set will not be Pareto optimal, although at least one such act must be. This would be the case if the group simply ignored the preferences of one or more of its members in arriving at a group choice. Hence Axiom 4 is a slightly weaker restriction on group choice than Pareto optimality.

Axiom 5 (Continuity). Let $\{a_n : n = 1, 2, \cdots\}$ be a sequence of acts in A and let $a_0 \in A$ be such that $a_n \gtrsim a_0$ for all n. If $\lim_{n \to \infty} \bar{u}_j(a_n) = \bar{u}_j(a_*)$, then $a_* \gtrsim a_0$.

This axiom says that group preference responds "smoothly" to changes in individual preferences, in the sense that if a small change is made in the preference index of one group member for a given act, it is possible to make small compensating changes in the preference indices of one or more other members such that the group preference ordering of the act is not affected. Put another way, the axiom implies that the group arrives at its preference ordering by making continuous trade-off decisions involving the preference indices of individual members.

Axiom 5 rules out so-called "lexicographic dictatorships," in which a designated group member controls the group choice so long as he has a definite preference; whenever he is indifferent, the choice passes to a second designated member, and so on.

95

Given the assumptions about individual preferences and Axioms 1 through 5 regarding group preference, we can prove the following

Theorem. There is associated with each member of the group a non-negative weight w_j such that, for any a', $a'' \in A$,

$$a' \begin{Bmatrix} > \\ \sim \\ < \end{Bmatrix} a'' \Leftrightarrow \sum_{j=1}^{N} \bar{u}_j(a') w_j \begin{Bmatrix} > \\ = \\ < \end{Bmatrix} \sum_{j=1}^{N} \bar{u}_j(a'') w_j \; ;$$

that is, group choice should be governed by the preference index defined by

$$W(a) \equiv \sum_{j=1}^{N} \bar{u}_j(a) w_j \; . \tag{7-4}$$

Our axioms are simply a reinterpretation of those used in Theorem 4.3.1 and Problem 4.3.1 of Blackwell and Girshick's *Theory of Games and Statistical Decisions*. Since the proof is given in that source, we will not repeat it here.

7.1.4. Scaling the Individual Weights

Our next task is to identify and interpret the weights $\{w_j\}$ which appear in (7-4) and indicate how they might be determined. Several procedures have been suggested in the literature; we will offer another one and in Sec. 7.1.7 we will compare our proposal with others.[4]

We will assume that each group member can contemplate a prize such that he is indifferent between receiving this prize and having the group choose the act which he *most* prefers. This prize can be considered as the inducement which would have to be offered to the member to persuade him to leave a group which has decided to adopt his most preferred act. Similarly, we will assume that each member can contemplate a prize which is indifferent to the act he *least* prefers.

Let an act a_j be such that:

     i. $\bar{u}_j(a_j) = \max_A \bar{u}_j(a)$,

     ii. $\bar{u}_k(a_j) = \min_A \bar{u}_k(a)$,   for $k \neq j$.

Then, by (7-4),

$$W(a_j) = \sum_{k=1}^{N} \bar{u}_k(a_j) w_k \; . \tag{7-5}$$

Further, let a^* be such that

$$\bar{u}_j(a^*) = \bar{u}_j(a_j) \; , \qquad \text{all } j \; ;$$

and let a_* be such that

$$\bar{u}_j(a_*) = \min_A u_j(a) \; , \qquad \text{all } j \; ,$$

and we note that

---

[4] Essentially the same procedure is suggested by Luce and Raiffa in *Games and Decisions*, p. 352, but without giving the necessary and sufficient conditions on group preference. We might mention that the constructive procedure for determining the weights which is outlined in the text suggests an alternative axiomatization of the group decision problem mathematically similar to the axioms for individual decision given by Pratt, Raiffa, and Schlaifer in the paper cited in note 1.

$$W(\lambda a^* + (1 - \lambda)a_*) = \sum_{k=1}^{N} \{\bar{u}_k(a_*) + \lambda[\bar{u}_k(a^*) - \bar{u}_k(a_*)]\} w_k \ . \qquad (7\text{-}6)$$

▶ The proof of (7-6) follows from (7-4) and the definition of the individual preference indices as follows:

$$W(\lambda a^* + (1 - \lambda)a_*) \equiv \sum_{k=1}^{N} \bar{u}_k(\lambda a^* + (1 - \lambda)a_*)w_k$$

$$= \sum_{k=1}^{N} [\lambda \bar{u}_k(a^*) + (1 - \lambda)\bar{u}_k(a_*)]w_k$$

$$= \sum_{k=1}^{N} \{\lambda[\bar{u}_k(a^*) - \bar{u}_k(a_*)] + \bar{u}_k(a_*)\} w_k \qquad ◀$$

The acts $a_1, \cdots, a_N, a^*, a_*$ can be constructed in the following manner. For each member of the group, ascertain a prize indifferent to his most preferred act and one indifferent to his least preferred act, as discussed in the second paragraph of this chapter. The act a^* gives each member the prize indifferent to the act he most prefers; the act a_* gives each member the prize indifferent to the act he least prefers; and the act a_j gives member j the prize indifferent to the act he most prefers and each other member the prize indifferent to the act he least prefers.

Suppose now that we offer the group a choice between the act a_j on the one hand and the probability mixture $\lambda a^* + (1 - \lambda)a_*$ on the other. For λ sufficiently high the group will prefer the probability mixture, while for λ sufficiently low it will prefer a_j. Our axioms of group preference imply that there is a unique λ_j such that

$$a_j \sim \lambda_j a^* + (1 - \lambda_j)a_* \ .$$

Representing a^* by the equivalent "mixed" act $\Sigma_{j=1}^{N} \lambda_j a^*$, we must have $\Sigma_{j=1}^{N} \lambda_j = 1$, since the theorem of Sec. 7.1.3 implies that

$$W(a^*) = W\left(\sum_{j=1}^{N} \lambda_j a^*\right) = W(a^*) \sum_{j=1}^{N} \lambda_j \ .$$

Now if we can determine the λ_j's for $j = 1, 2, \cdots, N$, we can conclude from the theorem of Sec. 7.1.3 that the weights must satisfy the system of equations

$$W(a_j) = W[\lambda_j a^* + (1 - \lambda_j)a_*] \ , \qquad j = 1, 2, \cdots, N \ . \qquad (7\text{-}7)$$

By reference to (7-5) and (7-6), we see that this is a system of homogeneous linear equations,

$$\sum_{k=1}^{N} (\delta_{jk} - \lambda_j)d_k = 0 \ , \qquad j = 1, 2, \cdots, N \ , \qquad (7\text{-}8)$$

where

$$\delta_{jk} = \begin{cases} 1 & j = k \ , \\ & \text{if} \\ 0 & j \neq k \ ; \end{cases} \qquad (7\text{-}9\text{a})$$

and
$$d_k = [\bar{u}_k(a^*) - \bar{u}_k(a_*)]w_k \; . \tag{7-9b}$$

Since $\Sigma_{j=1}^N \lambda_j = 1$, the matrix $[\delta_{jk} - \lambda_j]$ is of rank $N - 1$, and the cofactor of the element $\delta_{jk} - \lambda_j$ is λ_k. Hence, the system (7-8) is satisfied by the expressions

$$d_k = C\lambda_k \; , \qquad k = 1, 2, \cdots, N \; , \tag{7-10}$$

where C is an arbitrary constant. From (7-9b) and (7-10) we see that, for *given* individual preference scales, the weights w_k are determined up to an arbitrary factor of proportionality; or, equivalently, the *ratios* of the weights are uniquely determined.

Moreover, we can see by (7-9b) that the ratios of the weights are invariant under changes in origin of the individual preference scales, as required by Axiom 3, for, if we define new preference scales by $\bar{u}_k'(a) \equiv \bar{u}_k(a) + \alpha_k$ for all k, the α_k's will cancel in (7-9b), leaving the matrix $[\delta_{jk} - \lambda_j]$ unaffected.

The ratios of the weights are not, however, invariant under changes in unit of the individual preference scales. If we define new preference scales by $\bar{u}_k'(a) \equiv \beta_k \bar{u}_k(a)$ for all k, this will result in a reallocation of the proportional weight among the group members except in the special case $\beta_k = \beta$ for all k, in which all scales are changed proportionally.

It is tempting to think of the weights as reflecting the relative amount of "influence" each member exerts on the group decision, but the fact that the weights depend upon the particular units used to measure individual preferences shows that this interpretation would be misleading. It is more appropriate to interpret the weights as establishing an "interpersonal comparison of utility," in the sense that they make the individual preference indices "commensurable" so that they can be added to obtain group preference.

At this time, we should make an observation which will be developed in greater detail in Sec. 7.1.7. While our procedure can be thought of as leading to an "interpersonal comparison," it is not quite the same as the "interpersonal comparison" customarily eschewed in welfare economics. We are assuming only that the group can somehow make the ethical judgments involved in deciding which of two group members is to be benefited if a choice must be made; these judgments are the means of determining the weights and hence the interpersonal comparison. We are *not* asserting that there is a normative standard for interpersonal comparison which exists independently of the group's judgments in simple choice problems.

The constructive procedure for obtaining the weights described in this section takes on a particularly simple character if we scale individual preferences so that $\bar{u}_j(a^*) = 1$ and $\bar{u}_j(a_*) = 0$ for all j. From (7-9b), we then determine that $d_k = w_k$. Substituting this result into (7-8), we obtain

$$\frac{w_j}{\Sigma_k w_k} = \lambda_j \; ;$$

the relative weight allocated to member j is exactly equal to the indifference probability. It will be convenient to normalize the weights so that $\Sigma_k w_k = 1$.

7.1.5. Group Consensus of Preferences or Probabilities

As we observed in Sec. 7.1.2, we could have justified the assumption that a group "should" act as a maximizer of expected utility simply by postulating that the group "should" obey the individual decision-making axioms given in Sec. 7.1.2. This approach was deemed less satisfactory than that actually taken in Secs. 7.1.3 and 7.1.4. The theory of Sec. 7.1.2 involves such terms as "preference of act i given state *j*" and "personal probability of state *j*," which are difficult to interpret in the group context since, as we pointed out in Section 7.1.2, the members of a group are likely to differ among themselves in their assessments of "preferences" and "personal probabilities." The approach taken in Secs. 7.1.3 and 7.1.4 is more basic, taking into explicit account differences of opinion within the group. While formally similar to the derivation of "personal probabilities," this approach results in obtaining not "group probabilities" of states of the world but "weights" attached to individuals.

It is still of interest, however, to determine the conditions under which a group behaving in accordance with Sec. 7.1.3 can be considered as "maximizing expected preference" in the same sense as an individual behaving in accordance with Sec. 7.1.2. That is, we would like to be able to identify conditions under which there exist a set of "group probabilities" $P(\theta)$ depending upon the state of the world and a set of "group preferences" $u(a, \theta)$ depending upon both the state of the world and the act such that

$$W(a) = \sum_{\theta \epsilon \Theta} u(a, \theta)P(\theta) \ . \tag{7-11}$$

Combining the definition of the individual preference function (7-2) with that of the group preference function (7-4), we have

$$W(a) \equiv \sum_{j=1}^{N} \bar{u}_j(a)w_j$$

$$\equiv \sum_{j=1}^{N} \sum_{\theta \epsilon \Theta} u_j(a, \theta)P_j(\theta)w_j \tag{7-12}$$

$$= \sum_{\theta \epsilon \Theta} \sum_{j=1}^{N} u_j(a, \theta)P_j(\theta)w_j \ .$$

In order to reduce (7-12) to the form of (7-11), in which each term in the sum involves only θ, it is first necessary to sum out j. But since each term in the product $u_j(a, \theta)P_j(\theta)w_j$ as it stands depends on j, this summation must be taken over the entire product. As a result, it is not possible in general to express $\Sigma_j u_j(a, \theta)P_j(\theta)w_j$ as a product of two factors, one depending only on θ and the other upon both a and θ, as is the case with (7-11).

To avoid this difficulty, it is necessary to make either $P_j(\theta)$ or $u_j(a, \theta)$ independent of j, in order that it may be factored out of the summation. Suppose, for example, that $P_j(\theta) = P(\theta)$ for all j. This means that members of the group are in complete agreement on their probability assignments. Then (7-12) becomes:

$$W(a) = \sum_{\theta \in \Theta} \left(\sum_{j=1}^{N} u_j(a, \theta)w_j \right) P(\theta) = \sum_{\theta \in \Theta} u(a, \theta)P(\theta) \ , \tag{7-13}$$

the right-hand equation serving to define $u(a, \theta) \equiv \Sigma_j u_j(a, \theta)w_j$. Agreement on probabilities, then, is a sufficient condition for the group to act as a maximizer of expected preference, where the group utility given a state is a weighted average of the personal preferences.

Alternatively, let $u_j(a, \theta) = u(a, \theta)$ for all j. In other words, conditional on any state of the world, the members of the group would agree on preference assignments to acts. We will discuss this assumption further in the next paragraph, but we note that, if it is true, then

$$W(a) = \sum_{\theta \in \Theta} u(a, \theta) \sum_{j=1}^{N} P_j(\theta)w_j = \sum_{\theta \in \Theta} u(a, \theta)P(\theta) \ , \tag{7-14}$$

the right-hand equation serving to define $P(\theta) \equiv \Sigma_j P_j(\theta)w_j$. (The probabilities may require renormalization if $\Sigma_j w_j \neq 1$.)

The requirement of agreement on preferences involves more than that of agreement on probabilities. Individual preference numbers reflect not only preferences among acts but also attitudes toward risk, the latter as determined by choices among randomized acts. In order to reflect the conditional preferences of two individuals by the same set of preference numbers, we must show that they agree both on conditional preferences among simple acts and also on attitudes toward risk as reflected in preferences among randomized acts. Hence agreement on preferences assumes away two of the three reasons for lack of group unanimity which were cited in Sec. 7.1.2, while agreement on probabilities assumes away only one.

Marschak[5] defines a *team* as a group in which all of the members agree completely on their preference assignments to *acts*. The assumption that $u_j(a, \theta) = u(a, \theta)$ for all j is not, therefore, sufficient to define a team, since the agreement in the latter case is only conditional on the state of the world; differences in orderings of acts may still arise if the members disagree on the personal probabilities of states. We will call a group satisfying the condition $u_j(a, \theta) = u(a, \theta)$ for all j and a a *conditional team*. Hence, we have shown that a sufficient condition for a group to be a maximizer of expected utility is that it be a conditional team.

7.1.6. *A Bidding Group as a Maximizer of Expected Monetary Value*

By a slight specialization of the results of the last section, we can now justify the assumption, made in Chapters 3 through 6, that a bidding group should maximize the expected monetary value of its acts. The specialization involves the following three additional assumptions:

Assumption 1. Each act leads to a monetary return to the group as a whole which is conditional on the state of the world. We will denote the return

[5] "Towards an Economic Theory of Organization and Information," in Thrall, Coombs, and Davis, *Decision Processes*.

of the act a given the state θ by $M(a, \theta)$. The set of numbers $M(a, \theta)$ are agreed upon by all members of the group.

In order for this assumption to be correct, each state of the world must be described by a complete specification of all the factors which determine actual monetary return to the group. That is, a description of a particular state of the world in the bidding problem must specify as a minimum: (1) the bids of each of the other bidding groups; (2) all relevant characteristics of the market in which the bonds will be sold; (3) any other factors which any group member believes relevant to the determination of monetary return.

In a sense, Assumption 1 can be made tautologically true. If, for any listing of states of the world, we discover that the members of a group do *not* agree on the numbers $M(a, \theta)$, we must first ascertain the source of the disagreement. Having done so, we must then prepare a richer listing of states, in which the factor(s) leading to disagreement in the first listing have been incorporated into the description of each new state. This procedure might result in such complicated state descriptions, however, as to destroy the practical utility of the assumption.

Assumption 2. The jth member of the group receives a fraction z_j of the total monetary return to the group, where $z_j > 0$ for all j and $\Sigma_j z_j = 1$. The numbers z_j are independent of the state of the world and of the act.

(Although Assumption 2 may be approximately correct from a descriptive point of view, it may not be desirable as a normative proposition, since it precludes side payments, participation incentives, and other techniques which might be used to increase the preference of group members for a given external act).

The assumption that the proportions z_j are independent of the act chosen implies that the determination of participation is not part of the group decision problem. This is substantially true since, as we pointed out in Chapter 2, the manager of the group makes a preliminary determination of participation at the time he organizes the group. The final choice of act does have some effect on participation, however, whenever group members are permitted to drop out at the final price meeting or to take up "slack" left by drop-outs.

The assumption that the proportions z_j are independent of the state of the world is also not literally true. The members of the winning bidding group purchase the issue severally, not jointly, as noted in Chapter 2. As a result, strict proportionality regardless of the state of the world is true only of the purchase cost of the issue, the proceeds from group sales made by the manager, and cost incurred by the manager for group account. Other elements of monetary return depend upon each individual member's selling ability and cost structure, and these in turn may be influenced by the state of the world. Some members may, for example, be more adept than others at distributing bonds in a falling market.

According to assumptions 1 and 2, the monetary return of the act a to the jth group member given the state θ is $z_j M(a, \theta)$.

Assumption 3. The preference of each member of the group is a function of the monetary return to him only and is linear in monetary return within the range of possible outcomes of the bidding problem.

It is unnecessary to emphasize that this is at best only an approximation. The linearity of the preference function may, however, be a reasonably good approximation. Preference linear in money is typical of a neutral attitude toward risk. It is generally appropriate as an approximation when the amount at stake is small enough so that the relative riskiness of acts is not an influential consideration. One of the functions of the syndicate method in investment banking is to diminish the risk to any one banker by making the amount at stake relatively small. Hence the syndicate method tends to restrict the preference function of each participating member to an approximately linear segment. The success with which this objective is achieved undoubtedly varies from issue to issue. It is nevertheless of interest to examine the assumption of a linear approximation since it is probably not too gross.

We can now prove the following

Theorem. A group satisfying Assumptions 1–3 above is a conditional team with $u_j(a, \theta) = M(a, \theta)$ for all j.

▶ As a consequence of Assumptions 1–3, we have for all j

$$u_j(a, \theta) = \alpha_j + \beta_j z_j M(a, \theta)$$

for any real α_j and for $\beta_j > 0$. Since individual preference scales are determined only up to a positive linear transformation, we can define new preference scales by

$$u'_j(a, \theta) \equiv \frac{1}{\beta_j z_j} u_j(a, \theta) - \frac{\alpha_j}{\beta_j z_j}$$

$$= M(a, \theta) \; .$$

Since $u'_j(a, \theta)$ does not depend on j, the group is a conditional team. ◀

This last result permits us to conclude that a group satisfying Assumptions 1–3 as well as the axioms of Sec. 7.1.3 should maximize

$$\mathrm{E}\{M(a, \theta)\} \equiv \sum_{\theta \in \Theta} M(a, \theta) P(\theta) \; ,$$

where the probabilities $P(\theta)$ are defined by

$$P(\theta) \equiv \sum_{j=1}^{N} P_j(\theta) w_j \; .$$

The weights w_j are those appropriate when individual preferences are represented by $M(a, \theta)$ and which have been normalized so that $\Sigma_j w_k = 1$. (To obtain the weights, of course, requires that the group can consider hypothetical acts of a form excluded in the present context; hence we must assume that the nonavailability of the acts does not affect the weights.)

Since $P(\theta) = \Sigma_j P_j(\theta) w_j$, and since $P(\cdot)$ satisfies the axioms of probability theory, it might in some circumstances be appropriate for the group to assess P directly, rather than going first through the intermediate step of assessing the w's.

7.1.7. Comparison with Other Social Welfare Schemes

In this section, we will discuss briefly some alternative proposals for a group or social welfare function, contrasting them with the proposal advanced in the preceding sections. No attempt will be made to make this comparison exhaustive; the nature of the major differences will simply be sketched out.

First of all, we will consider Arrow's celebrated Possibility Theorem.[6] Arrow sets forth five desiderata for a social welfare function in the form of axioms. He then shows that no social welfare function exists satisfying all five axioms. It is clear, therefore, that the welfare function we propose must violate one or more of Arrow's axioms.

The essence of the difference is made evident by Arrow's alternative statement of his theorem:[7]

> *If we exclude the possibility of interpersonal comparisons of utility,* then the only methods of passing from individual tastes to social preferences which will [satisfy Arrow's other axioms] and which will be defined for a wide range of sets of individual orderings are either imposed [i.e., do not depend on preferences of group members] or dictatorial [i.e., depend on the preference of only a single group member].

In short, Arrow denies the possibility of interpersonal comparison of utility and is led thereby to deny the existence of a welfare function. We make no explicit assumption about interpersonal comparison but arrive at an expected welfare function which implicitly involves interpersonal comparison; see the closing paragraphs of Sec. 7.1.4.

Formally, Arrow's denial of interpersonal comparison is contained in his Condition 3. We quote Luce and Raiffa's rephrasing of this condition, which requires less new vocabulary:[8]

> *Condition 3* (independence of irrelevant alternatives). Let A_1 be any set of alternatives in A. If a profile of orderings [in A] is modified in such a manner that each individual's paired comparisons among the alternatives of A_1 are left invariant, the social orderings resulting from the original and modified profiles of individual orderings should be identical for the alternatives in A_1.

This condition need not be satisfied by our group preference function. It might be possible, for example, for some group members to leave an act unchanged in ranking but to lower its preference number (i.e., change the shape of their preference functions) in such a way that the group as a whole lowers it in ranking.

---

[6] Arrow, *Social Choice and Individual Values*, pp. 51–59.
[7] *Ibid.*, p. 59 (emphasis supplied).
[8] *Games and Decisions*, p. 338. The original statement of the condition may be found on p. 27 of Arrow, *op. cit.*

In other words, we permit individual preference numbers, as well as individual rankings, to affect group rankings of acts.

Arrow justifies his denial of interpersonal comparison on the grounds that individual preference scales are subject to too much arbitrariness to permit interpersonal comparison.[9] His argument is based primarily on the case of certainty in which individual preferences can only be determined ordinally. We, on the other hand, are interested in group decision making under uncertainty, and we use choices (both individual and group) among risky acts to establish the interpersonal comparison.

In our opinion, Arrow's Condition 3 is too strong—perhaps even too strong in terms of Arrow's own objectives. Interpersonal comparison is eschewed in welfare economics on the grounds that economists *qua* economists are incapable of making value judgments as to whether one individual should benefit at the expense of another. That is, there is no satisfactory *normative* concept of interpersonal comparison. Arrow's Condition 3, however, succeeds in also ruling out the possibility that the group itself can make these judgments. We do not believe that this possibility should be excluded, at least in the present context.

We can draw an analogy with individual decision making under uncertainty (i.e., without objective probabilities). According to the Laplace criterion for resolving such problems, each state of the world should be assigned the same probability and that act should then be chosen which maximizes expected preference relative to these probabilities. The Laplace criterion is a normative precept which attempts to prescribe behavior on purely logical grounds. We might wish to argue that there can be no purely logical basis for "comparing" states of the world (i.e., assigning probabilities to them), and yet we might be willing to accept the theory of personal probabilities discussed in Sec. 7.1.2, which relies in part on choices made by the decision maker in hypothetical situations to obtain the probabilities.

In large-group contexts, of course, the procedure we have suggested for obtaining a group expected welfare function might be totally impractical; the group could not even be made to agree on the simple choices necessary to calibrate the function unless *a priori* rules of procedure were provided. Even in small groups, it might be possible for group members to falsify their preferences. In such contexts, stronger conditions might be required, and we shall discuss some which others have suggested later in this section.

In passing, we note that our procedure may also violate Arrow's Condition 5 (Non-Dictatorship). As we pointed out in our discussion of Axiom 4, we do not exclude the possibility that one group member will have all the weight. As we also stated at that time, however, the exclusion of this possibility would not materially change the final results.

Next we consider an *n*-person generalization of Nash's bargaining model.[10] Nash, like Arrow, denies the possibility of interpersonal comparison of preference

---

[9] *Ibid.*, pp. 9–11.
[10] J. F. Nash, "The Bargaining Problem," *Econometrica* 18, pp. 155–162 (1950). The generalization is presented in Luce and Raiffa, *op. cit.*, pp. 348–350.

but, unlike Arrow, he makes use of individual preference scales. His approach leads to the criterion of maximizing the *product* of the individual group members' preferences. The act which maximizes the preference product is invariant under changes of unit in individual preference scales, and hence it is not necessary to single out a particular set of individual preference scales for comparison. The act which maximizes the preference product is *not*, in general, independent of the origins of the individual preference scales. In many group decision problems, however, there appears to be a distinguished alternative, i.e., the status quo, which obtains if the group cannot agree. If the individual preference scales are each transformed to a new origin at such a status quo point, then the Nash procedure identifies an optimal act which is independent of the origins of the (untransformed) scales.

It is evident that maximizing the preference product is not the same thing as maximizing a weighted average of preference. The critical difference comes in our Axiom 3, which is not satisfied by the preference product criterion if the latter is used to generate rankings of acts. This point is illustrated by the following example:

Preference of Member for Act

Member	a'	a''	a'''	$\frac{1}{2}a' + \frac{1}{2}a'''$	$\frac{1}{2}a'' + \frac{1}{2}a'''$
1	10	16	10	10	13
2	10	6	10	10	8
Preference Product	100	96	100	100	104

Since the preference product criterion identifies a' as superior to a'', if it is to satisfy Axiom 3 it must also identify $\frac{1}{2}a' + \frac{1}{2}a'''$ as superior to $\frac{1}{2}a'' + \frac{1}{2}a'''$, which it does not. In this example, in fact, the preference product criterion identifies a mixture of two acts as preferable to either one.

Several authors have suggested group preference functions involving weighting of individual preferences. Both Goodman and Markowitz[11] and Harsanyi[12] present axiom systems which are formally quite similar to ours. Goodman and Markowitz add another axiom, a symmetry condition, which requires that each group member's preferences enter into the final group preference with equal weight. This is not incompatible with our procedure since, as we noted in Sec. 7.1.3, what are determined uniquely by our procedure are not the weight ratios themselves, but their product with the individual preference scale parameters, $\beta_k w_k$.

Goodman and Markowitz go on, however, to suggest a procedure which would also determine the scale parameters uniquely. They propose that the psychological concept of "just noticeable difference" be used as a common scale unit for all individual preference functions. A discussion and critique of this proposal may be found in *Games and Decisions*, pp. 346–348.

[11] "Social Welfare Functions Based on Individual Rankings," *American Journal of Sociology 58*, pp. 257–262 (1952).

[12] "Cardinal Welfare, Individualistic Ethics, and Interpersonal Comparisons of Utility," *Journal of Political Economy 63*, pp. 309–321 (1955).

Based on the Harsanyi axioms and the work of several Dutch colleagues, Theil[13] has proposed another procedure for determining the weights. Like Goodman and Markowitz, Theil makes some additional assumptions beyond the basic axioms, of which the most critical (Theil's Postulate D) from our point of view is that the weights depend *only* on the $N \times N$ disutilities suffered by each member as a result of group adoption of another member's optimal act. In our notation, these disutilities are $\bar{u}_k(a_k) - \bar{u}_k(a_j)$ for all j and k. Theil's postulates result in the condition that the weight ratios must satisfy

$$\frac{w_j}{w_k} = \frac{\bar{u}_k(a_k) - \bar{u}_k(a_j)}{\bar{u}_j(a_j) - \bar{u}_j(a_k)} , \qquad \text{for all } j \text{ and } k . \tag{7-15}$$

It is not always possible to find weights satisfying these conditions; when it is not possible, Theil suggests several ways in which they may be approximately satisfied.

Theil's condition on the weight ratios may be compared with that derived from our expression (7-10), which gives

$$\frac{w_j}{w_k} = \frac{\lambda_j[\bar{u}_k(a^*) - \bar{u}_k(a_*)]}{\lambda_k[\bar{u}_j(a^*) - \bar{u}_j(a)_*]} , \qquad \text{for all } j \text{ and } k ,$$

or, since we lose no generality by letting $\bar{u}_j(a_*) = 0$ for all j, and since $\bar{u}_j(a_j) \equiv \bar{u}_j(a^*)$ for all j,

$$\frac{w_j}{w_k} = \frac{\lambda_j\bar{u}_k(a_k)}{\lambda_k\bar{u}_j(a_j)} . \tag{7-16}$$

These differences between Goodman-Markowitz and Theil on the one hand and us on the other may be summarized by stating that our procedure imposes fewer conditions of an *a priori* nature on the group criterion function. To make up for this, we must rely on the empirical evidence of observed group choices, as reflected in the indifference points λ_j.

7.2. The Group Decision Problem from the Manager's Point of View

7.2.1. *Contrast with the Preceding Section*

In Sec. 7.1 we treated the competitive bidding situation as a true *group* decision problem. The group evaluation of any act was considered to be a consensus of the evaluations of individual members of the group. In this context, it was sensible to talk of a group goal, e.g., the maximization of this group evaluation.

Quite a different tack will be taken in this section. We will no longer be concerned with group goals *per se*. Each individual group member will be assumed to be acting as a maximizer of his own expected utility, but within a limited range of alternatives.

Roughly speaking, we will be treating the group decision problem as an *n*-person non-cooperative game. The rules of this game are modeled after the

---

[13] "On the Symmetry Approach to the Committee Decision Problem," *Management Science 9*, pp. 380–393 (1963). See also Theil, *Optimal Decision Rules for Government and Industry*, Chapter 7.

actual price meeting described in Chapter 2, so that despite the non-cooperative label attached to the game it is probably a better description of reality than the cooperative model of Sec. 7.1.

As we will shortly see, the manager has a considerably richer set of strategic options in the group decision game than the other members. Therefore, we will approach the problem from the manager's point of view.

A glossary of the major symbols used in the remainder of this section follows. More detailed definitions will be given in context.

$d \equiv (p, b, c, y, r, s)$, a group external decision.

$z_i \equiv$ the assigned participation of i, $i = 0, \cdots, N$.

$\mathbf{z} \equiv (z_0, z_1, \cdots, z_N)$.

$a \equiv (d, \mathbf{z})$, a complete group decision.

$A_i \equiv$ the set of complete group decisions acceptable to i.

$S(a) \equiv$ the set of group members who will accept a.

$z_0^*(a) \equiv 1 - \sum_{\nu \in S(a)} z_\nu$, the manager's induced participation from a.

7.2.2. The Group Decision Game

The group decision game proceeds as follows: The manager chooses an act, consisting of a solution to the external decision problem of the group and an assignment of the proposed participation of each group member. The manager then announces his choice to the group. Each member of the group other than the manager then chooses either to "stick" (i.e., accept his proposed participation and the solution to the external problem) or to "drop out." As a result of the dropouts, there will be some "slack" (i.e., unassigned participation). We will at first assume that the manager has only the following options at a second move: (1) take up the slack himself and carry out the external decision; or (2) call off the deal entirely. The manager's decision problem is to choose an external act and an internal assignment of proposed participation in such a way as to maximize his own expected preference, given his judgmental probability assessments of how the other group members will respond to his act.

In Sec. 3.1 we defined a solution of the external decision problem as a set of fixed numerical values for each of the six external decision variables (price p, bid b, coupon rate c, yield y, cost of money r, and spread s) satisfying the system of equations (3.1). We will let $d = (p, b, c, y, r, s)$ be a solution and D be the space of all solutions.

If we let z_i represent the assigned participation of the ith group member and z_0 represent the assigned participation of the manager (both expressed as a fraction of par value), then we can represent the assignment of participation by an $N + 1$-tuple $\mathbf{z} = (z_0, z_1, \cdots, z_i, \cdots, z_N)$ such that $z_i > 0$ and $\sum_{i=0}^{N} z_i = 1$. We will let Z be the space of all such $N + 1$-tuples.

We will let A be the product space $D \times Z$ and $a = (d, \mathbf{z})$ be an element of A. At the manager's first move, therefore, he is to choose an $a \in A$.

For any $a = (d, z)$, let $S(a)$ denote the set of indices of the group members who will stick if the manager chooses the act a.

On the assumption that the manager takes up any slack left by dropouts, every $a \, \epsilon \, A$ determines the actual amount of participation the manager must take if the deal is to be carried through, as distinct from the amount z_0 assigned him by z. Denoting this actual position, or *induced participation*, by $z_0^*(a)$, we have

$$z_0^*(a) = 1 - \sum_{\nu \epsilon S(a)} z_\nu \, . \tag{7-17}$$

Let $\bar{u}_0(\cdot)$ be an expected utility function for the manager with domain A. We will assume that A includes that act a_0 representing "no deal" and that

$$\bar{u}_0(a_0) = 0 \, . \tag{7-18}$$

We will further assume that for any $a \, \epsilon \, A$ other than a_0, $\bar{u}_0(a)$ depends upon $z_0^*(a)$ as well as upon a directly. That is,

$$\bar{u}_0(a) = f(a, z_0^*(a)) \qquad \text{for all } a \neq a_0 \, .$$

Assuming that, for each a, the manager knows $z_0^*(a)$ with certainty, we would proceed as follows to find the best act from the manager's point of view. Define a subspace F of the space A by:

$$F \equiv \{a \, \epsilon \, A : \; f(a, z_0^*(a)) > 0\} \, . \tag{7-19}$$

Thus, F consists of those acts which the manager prefers to no deal at all, taking into account his induced participation for each act.

It is possible that F is empty, i.e., that $f(a, z_0^*(a)) \leq 0$ for all $a \, \epsilon \, A$. In this case the manager's optimal choice is to call off the deal. (Strictly speaking, if there is an $a \neq a_0$ such that $f(a, z_0^*(a)) = 0$, it might also be chosen.)

If F is not empty, the manager's optimal choice is that $a^* \, \epsilon \, F$ for which $f(a^*, z_0^*(a^*))$ is a maximum.

If a^* exists, it need not be unique. This will especially be the case if $f(a, z_0^*(a))$ depends on a only through the external decision d and the manager's induced participation $z_0^*(a)$. Under these circumstances, there will generally be a number of assignments of participation z which, when taken with a given d, will induce the same participation $z_0^*(a) = z_0^*(d, z)$. If as we have been assuming, the manager knew at the time he assigned participations exactly who would prefer to drop out on a given a, he could modify a by assigning 0 initial participation to all the dropouts and $z_0^*(a)$ to himself. This modified act would be just as desirable to the manager as a but would not entail any dropouts.

In practice, the manager may not be able to proceed in this way. For one thing, as we noted in Chapter 2, it is the usual practice for participation to be assigned at the time the group is formed, several weeks before the external group decision must be made. At the final price meeting, therefore, the manager's choice of $a = (d, z)$ is subject to the condition that z be a preassigned element of Z.

For another thing, even for given z the manager's induced participation $z_0^*(a)$ will generally be unknown to him at the time he selects a; the manager simply does not know enough about the preferences of the group members. Under these circumstances, the manager's objective must be to maximize the *expected* value of $f(a, z_0^*(a))$, providing it is positive.

An important function of the price meeting, as described in Chapter 2 is to enable the manager to learn something about $z_0^*(a)$.

7.2.3. *Graphic Illustration of the Manager's Problem*

The manager's decision problem in the group decision game is depicted graphically in Fig. 7.1. The horizontal axis represents the space A of acts. Alternatively, it can represent the subspace consisting of all elements of A for which the participation z is some preassigned element of Z. The vertical axis represents the manager's participation z_0. The line declining from left to right is the graph of the manager's induced participation $z_0 = z_0^*(a)$. (It is assumed that the elements of A can be ordered in such a way that $z_0^*(a)$ is a monotone function.) While $z_0^*(a)$ is shown as continuous in Fig. 7.1, if z is preassigned it is in reality a step function, changing its value whenever a moves into or out of an acceptance region.

The manager's preferences among (a, z_0) pairs is indicated on the graph by a family of indifference curves, each of which is the solution set of $f(a, z_0) = k$ for a particular value of k.

The following considerations were involved in drawing the indifference curves shown in Fig. 7.1:

Figure 7.1

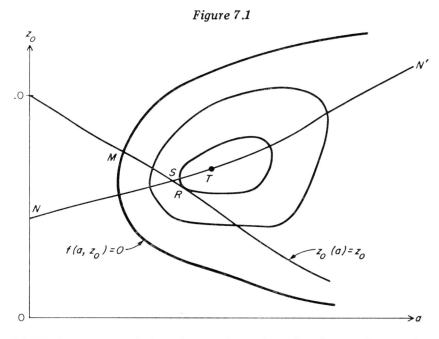

(1) We have assumed that the set A can be ordered according to the manager's induced participation; i.e., as we go from left to right the manager's *induced* participation decreases. Since a decrease in the manager's induced participation

means that other group members desire more participation, it is reasonable to assume also that the manager's *preferred* participation as a function of a (i.e., the z_0 which maximizes $f(a, z_0)$ for a given a) increases at least in a general way, as we go from left to right; this is the curve NTN'.

(2) Of all the points in the figure, the one least desired by the manager is that in the upper left-hand corner, where his induced participation is highest although his preferred participation is lowest.

(3) Although the manager's preferred participation increases from left to right, it does not follow that his preference for acts does also. Preferred participation reflects only the desirability of being in on a winning bid, since, if the bid does not win, participation is irrelevant. Hence, for given z_0, we would expect $f(a, z_0)$ to increase to a maximum as we move from left to right and then decrease. It will not fall below 0 to the right of the maximum, however, since failure to win the issue is no worse than failure to bid at all.

The heavier indifference curve which intersects $z_0 = z_0^*(a)$ at M is assumed to be the solution set of $f(a, z_0) = 0$. Hence, the set F defined by (7-19) consists of the segment of $z_0 = z_0^*(a)$ lying to the right of M. If $f(a, z_0) = 0$ failed to intersect $z_0 = z_0^*(a)$, then the set F would be empty and the manager's optimal choice would be "no deal."

If F is not empty, then the optimal act for the manager is found at the point where the indifference curve of highest value intersects $z_0 = z_0^*(a)$, such as point R in Fig. 7.1.

The principal difficulty encountered by the manager is that he does not know the location of $z_0 = z_0^*(a)$. A major function of the price meeting is to enable the manager to learn something about $z_0^*(a)$. By announcing successive values of a and polling the group members to determine the corresponding $z_0^*(a)$, he can approximate the location of the curve—assuming, that is, that the members give truthful responses, a matter we will discuss further in Sec. 7.2.5.

For each act, as noted above, the manager will have a preferred participation. In Fig. 7.1, the preferred participation is represented by the curve NN' which runs through the points where the manager's indifference curves have vertical slope.

As a first approximation, the manager could use the difference between his preferred participation and his induced participation as a measure of the non-optimality of the act. Thus, if his induced participation for a given act were greater than his preferred participation, he would "improve" the act in order to reduce his induced participation and increase his preferred participation.

This argument would lead to the choice of an act for which induced participation and preferred participation were equal, as represented by point S in Fig. 7.1. As can be seen, in general this procedure would not be optimal. Under the time pressures of the final price meeting, however, only a few "fixes" can be taken on the curve $z_0 = z_0^*(a)$. As a result, both points R and S can be located only approximately. Under these circumstances, the procedure which searches for S may not be without merit. It requires less detailed knowledge of the curves $z_0 = z_0^*(a)$

and $f(a, z_0) = k$, and it may lead to an act which is not materially less optimal than the alternative search for R.   The degree of non-optimality of this procedure is, of course, an empirical question on which, unfortunately, we have no data.

7.2.4.   Distributing the Slack Left by Dropouts

The analysis of the two preceding sections is unrealistic in one sense, in that it assumes that the manager is compelled to take up all the slack left by dropouts. Actually, as we observed in Chapter 2, improvement of the act usually leads some group members to increase their desired participations.   This permits the manager to distribute part of the slack to these other members.

Figure 7.2

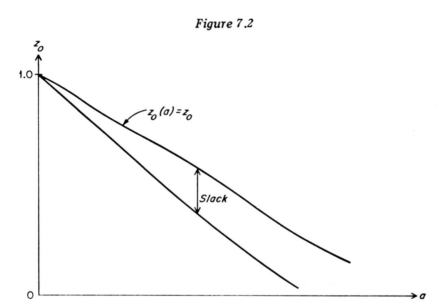

This situation is depicted in Fig. 7.2.   The manager now has access to the entire cone-shaped region indicated on the figure, rather than being constrained to the set F (the upper boundary of the region).   If the manager knows this region with certainty and if the maximum of the manager's preference function lies within this region, then his optimal act is to choose the a corresponding to this peak and to split up the slack with other members desiring increased participation.   If his peak lies northeast of the region, then his optimal act lies in the set F and he should absorb all the slack himself.   If his peak lies southwest of the region, then his optimal act lies in the other boundary of the region and he should give all the slack to other members.

It should be noted that unless the manager has access to the act he absolutely prefers (i.e., the peak of his preference profile), he should absorb either all or none of the slack.   This rule must, of course, be modified to allow for longer run considerations: if the manager fails to give a member some of the participation he desires, it may be more difficult to recruit this member for future groups.[14]

7.2.5. *Evaluation of the Syndicate Model*

One question of interest in connection with the group decision game is whether or not the solution arrived at by the manaser is Pareto optimal. That this question must generally be answered in the negative[15] is indicated by Fig. 7.3.

Figure 7.3

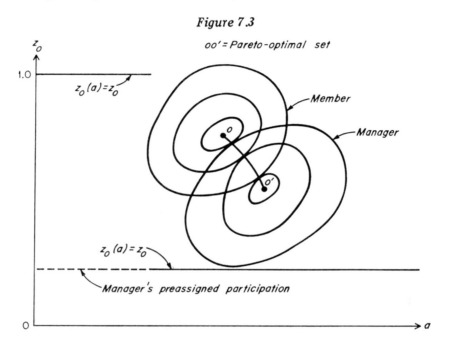

In this figure we assume that the group consists of the manager and only one other member. Indifference curves are indicated on the figure for both members. The Pareto optimal set consists of the points of tangency between the two families of indifference curves; the solution cannot be moved away from this set without affecting adversely at least one of the two parties.

---

[14] After the group decision problem was formulated by the author in the manner described in the last three subsections, the topic was considered by the Seminar in Applied Statistical Decision Theory at the Harvard Business School. As a result, Professor John W. Pratt considered the closely related problem in which the external act a is predetermined and the manager wishes to determine participations such as to maximize his own utility. Pratt showed that in general the optimal participations would *not* be of the "proportional shares" variety. If all individual utility functions are strictly concave, Pratt showed that there is an optimum in which the individual shares are increasing functions of the return realized by the group.

[15] In the related problem of Pratt discussed in the preceding footnote, the manager's optimum solution *is* Pareto optimal as regards the subset of all members excluding the manager. This is because the manager extracts any possible "surplus" from this subset in making his own decision, so that there are no profitable trades left for the subset to make within itself.

The amount of participation preassigned to himself by the manager is represented by the height of the horizontal line. The manager's induced participation will be equal to this if and only if the resulting act is within the acceptance set of the other member. This situation is indicated by the solid portion of the horizontal line. For other acts, the manager will be compelled to absorb the entire issue, unless he chooses to call off the deal altogether. Hence the set F also includes the solid horizontal line at the top of the figure.

It will be noted that the set F nowhere intersects the Pareto optimal set. Hence, so long as the manager is constrained to choose from F, the solution will not be Pareto optimal.

Another point which ought to be noted about the game is this. So long as the manager is compelled to search for the curve $z_0 = z_0^*(a)$, the other group members are not so much at his mercy as might appear at first. At any given announcement of an act by the manager, a group member could falsely reply that this act lies outside his acceptance region, hoping thereby to encourage the manager to move to a more favorable act. Of course, should the manager not do so, a member who falsified his acceptance region would find himself dropped from a deal he preferred to be in. Presumably members with relatively large preassigned participations are in the best position to take advantage of this tactic, because the manager would find it more difficult to get along without them than without some of the lesser members. Also, members who are polled near the end are in a less vulnerable position than those polled earlier; knowing the amount of slack left by the earlier replies, they are better able to judge whether or not the manager will be willing to take up the slack. (This suggests another possible "game": investment banking firms might be induced to change their firm names in order to be dropped down in alphabetical order!)

The desire on the part of group members to falsify their true preferences is probably fostered by the fact that the "yes" or "no" vote members are permitted is not adequate to reflect their true preferences among acts. As we pointed out earlier in reference to the manager, participation is relevant only if the bid is won. Since group members are asked only whether or not they desire to participate, they have no direct means of expressing an opinion on the probability that the given bid will win the issue.

In real bidding problems, the manager is able to get some additional information on individual group members' preferences through the medium of the preliminary price meeting (see Chapter 2). At this meeting, which takes place the day before the bidding, each member submits a ballot indicating his choice for offering yield and spread. Possibly this balloting could be extended to solicit additional information, such as:

(1) For a number of yield-spread combinations designated by the manager, each member could be requested to indicate his preferred participation. This would be useful to the manager in determining $z_0^*(a)$.

(2) Each member could be asked to rank the yield-spread combinations in order of preference. This would be useful to the manager in determining the member's evaluation of various bids.

The development of procedures for eliciting and processing better information on group preferences appears to be one of the more promising areas for further research on the bond bidding problem.

7.3. Summary of the Group Decision Problem

We have considered two alternative formulations of the group decision problem in this chapter. In the first formulation, discussed in Sec. 7.1, the decision-making process within the group is treated as a *bona fide* cooperative activity in which the final decision represents a sort of consensus of individual preferences. Granting certain assumptions, including that the amount of participation assigned to each group member is not a subject of group decision, we showed that expected monetary return is a reasonable criterion for group decision. The assumption that participation is preassigned is, except for the effects of "dropouts," consistent with normal syndicate practice, but it is not necessari.y desirable from a normative point of view. Side payments or other internal devices for sharing risk in other than strict proportion to participation may enable groups to reach positions preferred to those attainable with preassigned participation.

The unique position of the manager of a buying syndicate suggests that we might look at the group decision process as a game between the manager and the remaining members. This approach was explored in Sec. 7.2 and suggestions were advanced for optimal play by the manager. The manager is handicapped in searching for the optimum as a rule because his information about the preferences of the group members is very incomplete.

Either approach used in this chapter requires more information about individual preferences and probabilities than is generated by present syndicate procedures; the cooperative approach of Sec. 7.1 requires the most information. Because bidding decisions are made under very tight time pressures, it may be impractical or even impossible to obtain all of the information required within the time available. Nevertheless, it does seem feasible to obtain some information beyond that which is now obtained, and further research along these lines should have some payoff.

Bibliography

ARROW, K. J., *Social Choice and Individual Values*. New York: John Wiley & Sons, Inc., 1951.

——, S. KARLIN, and H. SCARF, *Studies in the Mathematical Theory of Inventory and Production Control*. Stanford: Stanford University Press, 1958.

BELLMAN, Richard E., *Dynamic Programming*. Princeton: Princeton University Press, 1957.

——, and Stuart E. DREYFUS, *Applied Dynamic Programming*. Princeton: Princeton University Press, 1962.

BLACKWELL, David, and M. A. GIRSHICK, *Theory of Games and Statistical Decisions*. New York: John Wiley & Sons, Inc., 1954.

BRACKEN, Jerome, and Arthur SCHLEIFER, Jr., *Tables for Normal Sampling with Unknown Variance*. Boston: Division of Research, Harvard Graduate School of Business Administration, 1964.

COHAN, A. B., *Cost of Flotation of Long-Term Corporate Debt Since 1935*. Chapel Hill: School of Business Administration, University of North Carolina, 1961.

COOMBS, C. H. See THRALL, R. M.

COURANT, R., *Differential and Integral Calculus*, 2d Ed. New York: Interscience Publishers, 1937.

DAVIS, R. L. See THRALL, R. M.

DEWING, A. S., *The Financial Policy of Corporations*. New York: Ronald Press, 1953.

DORFMAN, Robert, Paul A. SAMUELSON, and Robert M. SOLOW, *Linear Programming and Economic Analysis*. New York: McGraw-Hill Book Co., 1958.

FINANCIAL PUBLISHING COMPANY, *Bond Bidding Tables*. Boston: Financial Publishing Company, 1950.

FRIEDMAN, Lawrence, *Competitive Bidding Strategies*. Unpublished Ph.D. thesis, Case Institute of Technology, 1957.

GALSTON, Arthur, *Security Syndicate Operations*. New York: Ronald Press, 1928.

GIRSHICK, M. A. See BLACKWELL, David.

GOLDBERG, Samuel, *Introduction to Difference Equations*. New York: John Wiley & Sons, Inc., 1958.

GOODMAN, L. A., and H. MARKOWITZ, "Social Welfare Functions Based on Individual Rankings," *American Journal of Sociology* 58:257–262 (1952).

GRAYSON, C. J., *Decisions Under Uncertainty: Drilling Decisions by Oil and Gas Operators*. Boston: Division of Research, Harvard Graduate School of Business Administration, 1960.

HALSEY, STUART & COMPANY, INC., *Competitive Sales and Negotiated Public Offerings of New Public Utility, Railroad, and Industrial Debt Issues*. Undated pamphlet.

——, *The Development of Competitive Bidding for Securities Under State and Federal Jurisdiction*. New York, 1955.

——, *A Fifteen Year Record of Corporate Debt Financing in the United States*. Undated pamphlet.

HARSANYI, John C., "Cardinal Welfare, Individualistic Ethics, and Interpersonal Comparison of Utility," *Journal of Political Economy 63*, pp. 309–321 (1955).

——, *Rational Behavior and Bargaining Equilibrium in Games and Social Situations*. Unpublished manuscript, 1963.

Bibliography

INVESTMENT BANKERS ASSOCIATION OF AMERICA, *Fundamentals of Investment Banking*. New York: Prentice-Hall, Inc., 1949.

KARLIN, S. See ARROW, K. J.

KUHN, H. W., and A. W. TUCKER, *Contributions to the Theory of Games II*, Annals of Mathematics Studies 28 (1953).

LOSS, Louis, *Securities Regulation*. Boston: Little, Brown & Company, 1951.

LUCE, R. D., and H. RAIFFA, *Games and Decisions: Introduction and Critical Survey*. New York: John Wiley & Sons, Inc., 1957.

MARKOWITZ, Harry. See GOODMAN, L. A.

MARSCHAK, J. "Toward an Economic Theory of Organization and Information," in THRALL, COOMBS, and DAVIS.

MCKINSEY, J. C. C., *Introduction to the Theory of Games*. New York: McGraw-Hill Book Co., 1952.

MORGENSTERN, O. See NEUMANN, J. von.

NASH, J. F., "The Bargaining Problem," *Econometrica* 18:155–162 (1950).

———, "Equilibrium Points in *N*-Person Games," Proceedings of the *National Academy of Sciences*, U.S.A., 36:48–49 (1950).

———, "Two-Person Cooperative Games," *Econometrica* 21:128–140 (1953).

NEUMANN, J. von, and O. MORGENSTERN, *The Theory of Games and Economic Behavior*. Princeton: Princeton University Press, 1947.

PRATT, J. W., Howard RAIFFA, and Robert SCHLAIFER, "The Foundations of Decision Under Uncertainty: An Elementary Exposition," *Journal of the American Statistical Association 59*, pp. 353–375 (1964).

RAIFFA, Howard, "Arbitration Schemes for Generalized Two-Person Games," in KUHN and TUCKER.

———, and Robert SCHLAIFER, *Applied Statistical Decision Theory*. Boston: Division of Research, Harvard Graduate School of Business Administration, 1961.

———, See also LUCE, R. D.

———, See also PRATT, J. W.

SAMUELSON, Paul A. See DORFMAN, Robert.

SAVAGE, L. J., *The Foundations of Statistics*. New York: John Wiley & Sons, Inc., 1954.

SCARF, H. See ARROW, K. J.

SCHELLING, Thomas C., *The Strategy of Conflict*. Cambridge: Harvard University Press, 1960.

SCHLAIFER, Robert, *Probability and Statistics for Business Decisions*. New York: McGraw-Hill Book Company, 1959.

———, See also PRATT, J. W.

———, See also RAIFFA, Howard.

SHUBIK, Martin, *Strategy and Market Structure*. New York: John Wiley & Sons, Inc., 1959.

———, See also THOMPSON, G. L.

SIMON, H. A., "Dynamic Programming Under Uncertainty with a Quadratic Criterion Function," *Econometrica* 24:74–81 (1956).

SOLOW, Robert M. See DORFMAN, Robert.

THEIL, Henri, "On the Symmetry Approach to the Committee Decision Problem," *Management Science 9*, pp. 380–393 (1963).

———, *Optimal Decision Rules for Government and Industry*. Amsterdam: North Holland Publishing Co., 1964.

THRALL, R. M., C. H. COOMBS, and R. L. DAVIS, *Decision Processes*. New York: John Wiley & Sons, Inc., 1954.

TUCKER, A. W. See KUHN, H. W.

U.S. v. MORGAN, et al., *Analysis of the Volume of Security Issues, 1935–1949*.

———, *Transcript*.

WATERMAN, M. H., *Investment Banking Functions*. Ann Arbor: Bureau of Business Research, School of Business Administration, University of Michigan, 1958.